Almost Everything

Almost Everything

BOBBIE LOUISE HAWKINS

A CO-PUBLICATION BY

The Coach House Press
TORONTO, ONTARIO, CANADA

LongRiver Books
EAST HAVEN, CONNECTICUT, USA

Coach House Press
ISBN 0-88910-238-4 pb

LongRiver Books
ISBN 0-942986-00-8 hb
0-942986-01-6 pb

Distributed in the USA by:
Inland Book Company
22 Hemingway Avenue
East Haven, Connecticut
06512

Back to Texas was originally published by Bear Hug Books, 1977, USA. *Frenchy & Cuban Pete and other stories* was originally published by Tombouctou, 1977, USA and Verlag Gunter Ohnemus, 1980, Germany.

The editors wish to thank Chuck Miller for generously allowing his original illustrations for *Back to Texas* to be reproduced in this edition.

Special thanks to David Wilk, Michael Ondaatje, Mary Scally, Sarah Sheard.

Other books by the author

Own Your Body, Black Sparrow, USA, 1973)

Fifteen Poems, Arif Press, 1974

Trammel: Thought, Question, Treasure, Island, Canada, 1982)

Talk, radio play, PBS, 1980

Live at The Great American Music Hall, LP, Flying Fish, 1982.

A videotape of Bobbie Louise Hawkins reading is available from The Poetry Centre, San Francisco, SF, California.

Back to Texas

Frenchy and Cuban Pete

New Stories

Back to Texas

When you're stoned on grass ...

When you're stoned on grass and drinking wine and it's really festive ... a lot of people, eight or ten, and everybody feeling privileged and pleased to be there and to be so happy ... I'm talking about yesterday afternoon and evening. It was a birthday party. We were five of us waiting there for the birthday boy and the others and the cake and they all turned out to be about three hours late because of the traffic ... so we sat talking and enjoying it ... a fire in the fireplace ... and they did finally arrive; coming through the door. It felt like old-time family Christmases, waiting for the ones who lived farther away. And at some time during the evening ... the dilemma on grass if there's a lot of jazzy talking is to remember any of it later ... so this Sunday morning I started remembering it with pleasure and thinking I probably talked too much but not really feeling worried about it and there was a moment in it that suddenly I remember I said ... feeling really high and delighted to get it out at last ... I don't even know if it was true but it felt so accurate ... we had been talking about school's being narrower in some inverse ratio – like – the longer you're there the less it's got to tell you, and I remember saying the dues are worth it; all that's worth it ... and what suddenly came out that I'm remembering lying here in bed is – I said with all the certainty and pleasure of revelation, 'Nothing in my life ever happened that was as important to me as learning to read.'

And this morning I'm hung on remembering I said that as if the statement itself has turned to metal and I can hold it and gauge it; as if it were negotiable. A riffle like flip-cards in my mind of – wouldn't I pay it like a coin to have had this different or that different, as if that feeling, and being so definite saying it, really has to prove out.

My daddy was a good-looking woman chaser. He looked like Clark Gable and darkened his moustache with my mother's Maybelline mascara in private so he was angry when he saw the kid, me, standing in the bathroom door watching him.

Pictures of me then show me as a skinny, spooky kid. I was really quiet. If I broke a dish I hid it under the most complicated mess of crumpled paper I could make, filling the trash to hide my dangerous broken dish. He had a lousy temper and I never ... I guess I never will get rid of that secret self-protection I learned then.

They both were fighters, my mother and father. I remember him pulling the tablecloth off the table when his breakfast didn't suit him ... what a mess. And the time she threw a meat cleaver after him and it stuck the door jamb inches from his head. He stopped and she says he turned pale. But he left. Time and again he left and when he came back (it's called coming-back-home) after a few months or whatever time, they'd get along until they didn't.

We moved all over Texas, never more than six months in a place (usually it was closer to three or four) and they fought wherever they were together. So I never made any friends that lasted and everything was various depending on whether it was just my mother and me or whether my father was there; and whether they were trying to run a restaurant together or whether my mother was working as a waitress ... do you know that breakfast-shift, dinner-shift, swing-shift vocabulary? ... or there was once when she worked in a candy factory coating chocolates and putting the identifying little swirl on top. What I remember most often is that we were just the two of us living in a bedroom in somebody's house and my mother's salary would run ten dollars a week and the room plus board for me, and the landlady's looking after me, would run seven.

I don't mean to make this sound pathetic.

At some time during that, when I was five, I started school and I was a whiz. I went through the first and second grade the first year and I went through the third and fourth grade my second year and the third year when I was seven I was in the fifth grade and broke my arm twice so I got slowed down.

That would have been when we were in Mineral Wells. My father was with us then and we were living in a three-room house with a yard and honeysuckle on the porch at the bottom of a hill that's notable for a line of twenty-foot-high block letters filled with regular light bulbs that in the night glared out WELCOME toward the highway.

I loved that sign. It felt like being in church to stand at the base of those letters.

Just to finish that part of the story the next year we went to New Mexico and I went from being a whiz to passing the sixth grade 'conditionally.' I was a kind of half-dummy thereafter. I don't remember whether I had any notion of what went wrong. It feels like years of chaos.

My father finally truly left around then. We sat in my Aunt Hannah's house south of Albuquerque and he roamed in the night around the house yelling Mae and my Uncle Horace would yell back Mae doesn't want you anymore, and I've got a .22 here, and my father finally left for good.

But, while I feel like that has to be told somehow, these few pages going the way they've gone, what I really want to mention and it took me until yesterday to get it into the air, is that all that time, and right from the first, reading was my darling pleasure.

I've always been impressed ...

I've always been impressed by the ability some people have to remember everything, things from a long time back, the name of a first grade teacher, whatever.

What I have instead is page after page of random notes to remind me.

Miz VanArt with the gun under her pillow and bullet holes in her door eating squabs in Mineral Wells

horny toads

the old man throwing his shoe through the window and putting shoe polish in his nose

the lady with the crazy daughter

In a book like this, the 'plot' is whether it can come together at all. It might help to think of it as having *gathered* more than having been written. It's got about as much plan to it as tumbleweeds blown against a fence and stuck there.

Last October ...

Last October for the first time in more than twenty years I went back to Texas.

I went from San Francisco to my mother's house in Albuquerque and the next day about mid-morning the two of us left there driving her three-year-old air-conditioned Buick, headed east.

'We're going to have the sun beating on our backs all the way to Cline's Corners,' she said. And, 'Honey, get Mama a cigarette. They're in my purse. Do you want to drive?'

'Sure, if you want me to. You sure it won't make you nervous?'

'I'll just get us through the city limits. I know how all these freeways go.'

'Are you supposed to smoke cigarettes?' I handed her the one I had lighted.

'Oh, I'm not supposed to but it won't hurt anything. Just, I'm not supposed to smoke so much that I get to coughing. Any kind of a cough plays hell with my throat.'

When we were into the Sandias east of the city where the freeway turns into a more old-fashioned highway she pulled over and stopped to let us switch places.

'This car handles *really well* at fifty-five,' she told me.

'O.K. Mama.'

She began an instantaneous nesting in the midst of Kleenex, brought out chewing gum, put her purse where she could get it.

I put the seat back a couple of inches, checked the rear view mirror, pulled out onto the tartop.

'You're just used to those *little* cars that don't have much power,' she said. 'This car'll creep right up on you if you don't pay attention. You'll think you're just poking along and if you look at the speedometer it'll be on eighty or ninety.'

She pulled a plastic package of slippers out of the glove compartment and exchanged her high heeled shoes for them. She clicked the radio on.

The radio has a way of acting like a messenger. They play so many songs that if you're in any kind of a particular 'catch' there's bound to be one that starts rising up above the rest like it's got your name on it.

If the song is at all popular it seems like that's the only thing they're playing after awhile.

Merle Haggard came in on us singing that song that has the line in it *Sing me back home, turn back the years* ... That song was number one all the time we spent driving around. We kept car company for just under three weeks, me, Mama, and Merle. It was like old times.

Used car salesman ...

Used car salesman, itinerant preachers and fry cooks have a hard time getting credit: bad risks, too mobile.

Amarillo, Lubbock, Abilene, San Angelo, Sweetwater, Houston, Galveston; my daddy was a six foot three Irish frycook. We followed the general rule. On short notice or no notice at all he'd have Mama and me in the car and gone. When he ran out of towns he'd just start over.

It wasn't until many years later, I mean quite recently, that it occurred to me to wonder how many of those abrupt departures had to do with jealous husbands; or to a woman whose demands were finally strong enough to override his charm.

'Are you feeling carsick, Jessie? Jack, Jessie's feeling carsick! Here honey, trade places with me. Hang your head out the window. The wind on your face'll do you good. Pull over, Jack! She's going to vomit! You better stop the car!'

There I'd be, shoved out the window of the car as it veered to the side of the road ... my mother pushing me farther out at the same time she clutched my skirt. My father, resentful and swearing, would slam the car to a stop and I'd stand beside the road in the settling dust, retching green bile.

'She's bilious! I told you in Brownfield that we should stop and eat something!'

Jack looks, disgusted, at the side of his car, pulls up a young cotton plant to wipe at the side of his car.

His name was Walter but he called himself Jack. It was the current hero name. Jack Armstrong, the All-American Boy was a radio favourite. A current song was Cowboy Jack:

> Your sweetheart waits for you, Jack
> Your sweetheart waits for you
> Out on the lonely prairie
> Where skies are always blue

And she always did. In every town.

Breaded veal cutlets, flour and milk gravy, shrunken peas, a wilted lettuce leaf with a slice of tomato and a big dab of mayonnaise going a darker yellow at the edges ... all over Texas.

(You know, nobody wanted that place. Time and again the U.S. turned it down. Aaron Burr wanted it for awhile but Jefferson ruined him. James Monroe let Texas go by to get Florida. Daniel Webster resigned as secretary of state when President John Tyler started considering it. That great patriot-author Edward Everett Hale wrote a sixteen-page pamphlet against 'the introduction into the Union of an unprincipled population of adventurers, with all the privileges of a state of naturalized citizens.' The title of that pamphlet was How To Conquer Texas, Before Texas Conquers Us.)

Mineral Wells: Jack takes the tablecloth (one of many times) and with a pull crashes breakfast onto the floor; dishes, eggs, bacon, gravy, biscuits, and a full pot of coffee.

Galveston: Handsome Jack springs to the aid of the blonde young woman who stands ... ('I know that type,' Mae snorted to a friend of hers enroute to the lake, 'she's going to move two inches into the water and say I wish somebody would teach *me* to swim.') ... ankle deep in the water, looking at him archly, her arms wrapped around herself, pretending to shiver. 'I wish somebody....'

Abilene and Austin: Handsome Jack breaks his wife's nose two separate times in different towns.

Lubbock: Jack looks back to see the meat cleaver thrown by his wife quiver in the door frame inches from his head.

And in which of those towns did Jack go down on one knee and hold his arms open toward me, saying, 'Are you going to leave your daddy, honey?' And I came flying back while Mae stood at the door with her suitcases packed.

'Alright then,' she said into my tears, 'but someday *you're* going to want to leave him and when you do we'll go.'

Children are so easy to get around.

Once he held two coins out to me, a nickel and a dime.

'Which one do you want,' he asked, 'the big one or the little one?'

Of course I knew the difference and I took the dime and saw the disappointment on his face.

'Why do you want that one? This one is bigger.'

So, seeing that he really wanted me to take the nickel I put the dime back and took the nickel and he got on with his joke.

'Look here,' he yelled to my mother, 'she took the nickel instead of the dime because it's bigger!'

One of the best times ...

'We should be at Cline's Corners in about ten minutes.'

'I believe it's right over that hill yonder, babe. You go straight ahead on the ridge and then circle back.'

Mama went on with her story. 'One of the best times that I remember when we were kids was when we lived out there south of Abilene on a farm. We had a big old two-story farmhouse with a great big earth tank down at the back. There was a spring above that fed into it. This big old tank had a gravel bottom and fresh water run into it all the time out of this spring. Then on the far side there was a place that it run out. That earth tank was us kids' joy and pleasure. We'd swim in it all summer then we'd skate on it all winter. We'd go down there and build us a big fire on the bank. We'd go out on that ice and skate and slide until we was tired and cold. Then we'd go get warm at the fire. We used to take eggs down there to boil in a bucket or some kind of meat to cook on a stick over the fire.

'In the fall after the feed had been gathered and brought in our stepdaddy would take these great big field rakes — it's like a plough — you pull it with horses ... and he'd start at one end of that field and he'd rake all the stalks to the centre of the field. There'd be a pile of stalks four or five feet high and real wide, five or six feet, and it would go all the length of the field which was ... heavenly days ... a *good* mile long!

'We'd wait until some night when the wind was in the right direction and we'd get the neighbours' kids that was our ages to come over ... it was when the wind would be blowing from one end of that pile to the other end ... that direction. We'd start burning that pile at one end and we'd stay down there until it had burned across the whole length of the field which normally took until the wee small hours of the morning. We'd play games around the fire and take food down there to cook.

'We really had a fine time when we were little ones and had a chance to have it,' her voice was wistful.

'What made all that change?'

'They had an influx of grasshoppers. It was four or five years in a row that the grasshoppers ate *everything*. They ate the feed. They ate the cotton. They'd just ... you know ... as the little cotton came out of the ground they'd just bite it off right down at the ground. This happened for three or four years.

'It wasn't just us. It was *everybody* in this whole area.

'At the time it started we had fourteen nice milk cows plus all the calves that we had for beef, and young bulls. And we had chickens and pigs, the things you keep to kill off.

'The first two or three years, well, the *first* year we did alright on the proceeds of former crops. Then the next year my stepdaddy had to borrow some money from the bank to make a crop. Alright, they got wiped out by the grasshoppers again *that* year. Everybody did. Then the next year *everybody* borrowed toward a crop. Everybody was in the same position that third year because the bankers in self-defense had to lend the money for crops because it was their only hope of getting their money back.

'Then when it happened again the next year, well, the farmers either had to turn over everything they had to the bank, their farming tools and cattle and all, or they had to sell it all for next to nothing. Whatever they had the banks took. It was bad all the way around.

'So at that time everybody moved to towns to try and get work because there wasn't any work on the farms.'

'Would that have been around the time that Peter was nine? Was that why he had to go off and saw wood?'

'No, he didn't have to. He did that because my stepdaddy was so mean to him that he just couldn't stand it any longer. He just got up and left. But my stepdaddy did have a nice son that was our stepbrother. That's where Peter went. What *he* was doing ... yes, come to think of it that was during the same time ... what the stepbrother was doing, he went way back into wooded country and he cut wood for people that had wood stoves, which was most people. Then they would haul it to whoever wanted it or they'd take it to the wood yard in the town.'

'Look. There's snow on the mountains over Santa Fe.'

'First snow of the season. If I remember it right we got it even earlier last year.'

'So then you moved to town?'

'My stepdaddy got some kind of job. I don't remember what. Oh, one thing, he was one of these what they used to call faith doctors.'

'He was?'

'Yeah he ... uh, cool it a little, babe. You'll be right there in a minute. Top of the bridge. Now it's the next one.

'Yeah, he did a lot of people a lot of good. For instance there was this one man that come to him that had his toes curled under just like this.'

She held her hand out with the fingers under to show me.

'Oh, honey, you can just go straight ahead and then take a left,' she interrupted herself.

'I should go right shouldn't I?'

'You *can* go either one but if you go left we'll come out at Cline's Corners and get us a Coke.'

'O.K.'

'It's easier than making that big swirl.

'This man's toes had been that way for *years*. My stepdaddy worked with those some way and talked to that man and when he got through ... this man had told him he'd give him *any* amount of money if he got those toes straightened out. He got those toes straightened out and the man give him ten or fifteen dollars.'

The Irish came to Texas ...

The Irish came to Texas building the railroads as they came, the cheapest labour available. There were some Chinese and some Negroes but mostly that company of men was filled out of the latest wave of Irish to hit the country. Hardly arrived, eyes still full of ... think of it ... the pictures you've seen of Ireland if you've never been there. All that soft green and blue hazed over by mists ... deep valleys with fog ... lakes ... all that growing green stuff.

And think of the Great Plains; land flat as a table and immense, far as the horizon; the sky an inverted bowl to hold the tiny work gang in, like ants; the sky huge and pale blue with chicken hawks gliding in slow circles, held up by the rising heat.

For another instance: St. Patrick drove the snakes from Ireland, but Texas has all four of the poisonous snakes to be found in the U.S. (rattlesnake, coral snake, water moccasin and copperhead.)

This is, as it's clear, a fantasy of that time and place and those persons but few things are probable. They lived in a mess of shacks and material, in the simple fact of backbreaking work. And every morning a huge sun rose to blast them; the rails too hot to touch; the muscles and haul of getting them into place. And when a man straightened to ease his back he must have had that perspective line of the rail that had already been laid stretching back in a perfect pointer, himself on the balance end of it; lips cracked, dry skin turning to leather in a sirocco sandstorm; still heat with twisters on the horizon in season. ('The old man was so scared of tornadoes that he'd have us kids and mama all crammed together in the storm cellar most of the night all through the season. We wouldn't no more than get to sleep before he'd be dragging at the covers and swearing at us.')

Many of them took Cherokee women. That nation, the Cherokee nation, got dispersed so early and the women weren't secured.

What I really have on my mind just at this minute is how that Irish-Cherokee got seeded out across that vast distance by the time they had stopped. There's a high percentage of residents across the Texas plains who've got that mix in them.

There must have been a lot of interplay ... I mean that both those lots of people believed in visionary realities at least part of the time. And it hangs on. The Hardshell Baptists, the Holy Rollers, the snake handlers. My grandmother has second-sight and my Aunt Ethel has the gift-of-tongues.

But there are other aspects to it. My Aunt Ethel waited to claim her

23

own son in a dime store in a one-street Texas town some forty years ago because two women, as they passed by him, said Look at that cute little Indian boy. She waited until they were at the far end of the store and couldn't see her hurry him out and home. One of her younger sisters was there and saw it all, got hustled out as well, and there was at least the looseness to let it turn into a family joke.

I get to talking ...

'I get to talking and let the car get down to fifty-five,' Mama said.

'Well, we got through town,' I answered.

'We'll be in Texas pretty quick. Did I tell you about the time I brought Maggie and Rachel over here? They were just little bitty things, you know, and I brought them over here. I had told them that all my people lived in Texas. We got up there to that sign ... you know that stone map shaped like Texas? I said to them, You see that? That means we're in Texas! Of course there wasn't a thing there except wide open country. Maggie raised up and looked all around and she said, Well! Where is everybody?

'But if Rachel didn't show her ass over there! You know how she can when she gets on one of them tears.

'I had a real nice setup. I bought 'em funny books. They got in the back seat and I turned on the air conditioner. In the car we just had a ball.

'The minute we got over there ... I thought they would *play* with the kids ... the big kids ... which *they* wanted to. But nossir! Rachel would *not* do it. She wanted my attention every minute.

'I was trying to visit with Hannah, trying to visit with Ethel, trying to visit with Peter and Maxine and here she come ... for the fiftieth time in the hour ... I said, Well honey, it'll be alright! I said, Don't get so fussed up over it. Just go ahead and play. She *jumped* up and down, and went to *screaming* at the top of her voice. She said, You don't *like* me! and I *hate* you! You're not my grandmother *anymore!* You'll *never* be my grandmother again because *I hate you!* You're not even my *friend!!*

'Brother! I went outside ... I didn't get a *big* one ... I got a little bitty keen elm switch and I come back in there and I went to *work* on her with it! I said, I *am* your grandmother and I *do* love you and you *do* love me!! *Right?* And she said, Yes, grandmother, yes.

'Then she went home and told you that I whipped her with a whip! It was just a little old keen switch because I didn't want to do her too much damage. I had to get her about three times! I never saw her act like that in my life!

'She's got to learn to control it or she'll never have anything but hell on earth. That's Ethel exactly! That's Ethel the way she was when she was a kid!'

'Oh yeah?'

'No ... (musing) I don't remember Ethel throwing temper fits like that till after she was grown and married. (laughing) But boy, she goes off on them now!

'She told me about her and Hannah getting into a squabble and she said, "I got so mad at her that I just couldn't think what to say to her" ... and she was just dying laughing ... "And I told her she was a *liar* and a *thief!*"

'I said, Ethel, you and I have never got mixed up that bad yet but if we ever do you better be smart and not call me either of those names! I said, Because the day you do you and I are going to tangle!'

'I think that sounds pretty mild.'

'A *liar* and a *thief?*'

'Yeah, when you get as angry as you can get and the best you can come out with is something like a liar and a thief....'

'Oh, she wouldn't think of saying bitch or son-of-a-bitch or something like that.'

'I bet it relieved her to say it. She enjoyed it later.'

'Yeah. I told her I said, Ethel, you know what I'd of done if I'd've been Hannah? Ethel said, No. I said, I would've never spoke to you again as long as I lived! You'd of been right off the board as far as I was concerned if you'd of called me a liar and a thief.'

'That's a good song, that Merle Haggard song.'
'Oh. What song is that, honey?'

What were we talking about ...

'What were we talking about?'

'You were telling me about when you and Horace and Hannah spent the winter in east Texas,' I answered.

'I can't get too *interested* in telling about that.

'Well, Hannah and Horace they was going down there because the doctor had told Horace that the paint was starting to affect his lungs and cause him problems with his breathing. So they come by and got you and me from Peter's and Maxine's, I guess, when they lived at Hawley. Then we went down into southeast Texas.

'And Horace was ... oh ... we found this great big old farmhouse, you know, just on a lovely ... a big old house ... It belonged to his family. Lots of land around it and lots of dead trees, mesquite trees, and a *huge* fireplace, almost a walk-in thing, really big, natural stone. They took a trailer with beds and bedsteads and cooking pots and pans and a gasoline stove. We set up our kitchen and living room in this big room with the fireplace.

'And the ... oh ... we'd have the best meals! This was a big ranch and his people ... well you know at that time if anybody needed beef they just killed a calf and dressed it out and divided it around among the family. Then when they needed another one they'd do the same thing. So they furnished us with all kinds of fresh meat, lots of Rhode Island Red eggs ... you know those brown eggs ... and milk and butter and cream. You never saw the like. Just running over.

'Horace cleared one room there by the fireplace ... by the *room* with the fireplace ... and he took the car and the trailer ... little two-wheeled trailer ... and he went out ... He just brought in great loads of those dead logs and filled that room up with them.

'It would come big snows and we'd just build big roaring fires in the fireplace. It was more fun. The people around there would give dances. Somebody would clear out a couple of great big rooms and the local musicians would play for the dance and we'd go and we'd dance all night. Stop at midnight for a barbecue dinner or something like that and after we all got through eating we'd dance until morning, then we'd all go home.

'It come big snows! It'd just come *big* snows and everything'd be covered, all those pretty trees. We really enjoyed it. We'd put on rubber boots and heavy coats and get out, Hannah and me, and take walks thru the snow.

'Horace set him out a trapline, just an old-fashioned trapline and he'd go out and walk his trapline every day. He'd catch coyotes, skunks ... they have beautiful fur, of course, in the wintertime ... coyotes have beautiful fur too. There was two or three other kind of animals. I don't know whether there was any foxes but it seems like he got a few fox furs. He did that for a pastime and that paid for all our expenses!'

'How old were you all then?'

'Well ... you was six months old ... wait a minute ... you was eighteen months old so that made me about nineteen. Hannah was about twenty-one or twenty-two and Horace was ten years older ... eleven ... He was eleven years older'n Hannah. He'd have been about thirty-two or three.

'They had these huge fieldstone storage rooms there, like a big barn. Horace kept his furs and things out there, the pelts, stretched out over boards, and he cured them out there. Seems like we stayed there ... we stayed down there about six weeks.'

'Did it help his lungs?'

'Oh yes, he got alright. He hadn't been down or anything. The doctor just told him it was best for him to get away from that paint for awhile.'

My Uncle Horace had ...

My Uncle Horace had eyes as pale as water and the greatest private playhouse in the world. Of course he called it a *store house* ... the old barn. And the reasons he gave me and Sonny as to why we should stay out were reasonable. Dryrot: the barn was bound to have dryrot and we could fall through the loft floor and injure ourselves drastically. Tetanus: since all the doors were padlocked shut our entry was gained by climbing the accumulation of cast-off machine parts, old bedsprings and junk in general that was stacked against the back of the barn and piled high enough to let us reach a square loft door. Uncle Horace projected the results of a scratch from that metal as if it had all been soaked in whatever the poison is that pygmies or whoever it is tip their arrows with. He had other reasons but they're less sensational and harder to remember.

What never got stated was what everybody knew. Horace was one of those people who can't stand to throw anything away but he couldn't live in the midst of it all. So he 'stored' it. The barn was a symbol for a kind of peace of mind. He was keeping the residue of his life secure there. Old books of wallpaper samples, mail order catalogues with fabric swatches glued to the pages, fencing foils; it drove him wild to learn that we had been there. Once when we were high up a tree and keeping quiet to avoid doing dishes we saw him come from the house, realize we weren't in sight and head for the barn ... almost on tiptoe. He put his ear to the wall to hear us, but there wasn't any sound. Up the tree we kept quiet. He took his keys out and unlocked one of the doors. We could hear him inside moving around the piles of boxes and trunks, looking to see whether we were hidden. For him I guess it was desperate.

For our part, we were fans of the Katzenjammer Kids, Pirates, Robin Hood; and we were cronies. Such a sight as Uncle Horace scouring out the hiding places in the barn was a kind of triumph for us.

He was a decent man but he was easy to bypass.

You knew...

'You knew he shot himself?'

'I knew he shot himself,' I answered.

'But honey, poor thing, he's better off.'

'I never understood, when he went into the hospital what exactly was the matter with him?'

'Well, the thing of it was he had started to Idaho to see Florence and the kids and spend Thanksgiving with them. He got to ... not Cortez, Colorado ... but up in that area and he had a stroke. He *knew* something had happened to him so instead of stopping *there* and going to a Vets hospital ... or *any* hospital and giving the Veterans the bill he turned around and drove his car back to Albuquerque and went into the Vets hospital there.

'Bert what's-his-name, that electrician that was a friend of his called me up one day and said, Mae, have you seen or heard anything from old Horace? And I said, No, I sure haven't. And he said, Well, he started for Florence's and that's the last I heard, said, He hadn't been home and I tried to call him at Florence's and he hadn't been there ... hadn't heard from him in months.

'So Florence called me or I called her, I don't remember which and anyway her daddy never got there. So none of us couldn't figure it out. I called Hannah and Bud. Bud didn't know anything. So Bert one day said he just happened to think maybe he's up at the Veterans hospital. So he went and checked. Horace was there and he'd been there a month.'

'Why didn't Horace get in touch with somebody and tell them he was there?'

'He was just too sick or he didn't have the mind for it. You see a car on this side?'

'Naw ... well ... yeah, but it's way up there.'

'It's not far enough that I'd have time to go around this truck.

'He had a blood clot lodged between his heart and his kidney and it was running his blood pressure up so high that it was real dangerous. So, anyway, they had to go in there and get it and that was when his brother Wendell come up to be there.

'They went in there to get it and they'd give him so much blood thinner stuff trying to dissolve it that after the operation the blood would just run out around those stitches. It'd collect in here ... just a *ball* of it ... a *pile* of it in his stomach ... and they'd have to go in there to get it out. They operated on him three times in three days. The third time I told Wendell I said, For god's sake tell that stupid doctor to put a drain tube in there to drain off the excess blood. They can always give him more blood but he *cannot* stand them going in and out and in and out, you know. So the doctor come in to talk to us and Wendell asked him about that and he said, Why, I hadn't *thought* about *that*. So they put in a drain tube.

'By that time they were giving him a blood coagulant but they'd already give him so much of the other stuff that they just cancelled out.

'Then his kidneys failed. They had to put a bunch of stuff in him to try to purify his kidneys, his urine or something.

'The last time they brought him out of there they told me, they said, There's something wrong with one of his legs. He acts like one of his legs is paralyzed. I said, Well, it couldn't be nothing except another blood clot. It was behind his knee and they left it go. They waited until he had gangrene in his foot before they ever done anything. It was moving right up his leg. Honey, it was as purple as if you'd painted it with purple ink.

'By that time Wendell had gone home and he'd left a written thing up there that if there was anything anybody in the family had to sign they were to let me sign it. They called me at 7:30 one morning ... no ... they called me one night to tell me to be up there at 7:30 the next morning and I'd have to sign a thing for them to take his leg off. Boy, what a hardship. That like to have *killed* me. I went up there and I told them ... see, he was in the intensive care unit ... and I said, I'm not signing *anything* until I see that leg *myself*! They took me right in there and, Jessie ... his foot and his leg was purple just on a slant to his knee. They was going to take his leg off below his knee and it just so happened that they had a real good specialist in this line of stuff that had flown in that morning from Chicago or somewhere and he said, Oh no! He said, You take that leg off below the knee and you'll have to go in again and take it off way up here. So he went in and he took it off right here. So he got it.

'Poor Horace. He'd had so much pentathol. That stuff'll drive you crazy. You get a certain amount of brain damage from that the way it cuts your respiration. It cuts your blood pressure and slows you heart down. You don't get enough blood and oxygen to your brain. That's the reason I get these hallucinations after I've had too much of it.

'After my last operation when Alice come to visit me she was sitting in a chair near the bed and I started chuckling and she said, What are you laughing about? And I said, I'm going to tell you I know it isn't true so you won't think I'm crazy but I just saw the most beautiful white cat in the world come through the window and jump onto the floor and go under your chair. And she *jumped* up and started looking all around for that cat. I said, Alice, it's *bound* to be a hallucination. We're three floors up!

'Anyway, I'd go up there to see Horace, poor thing, and he'd talk plumb crazy more often than not. I'd take him stacks and stacks of magazines. You remember how he loved to read magazines? Everybody I knew give me magazines to take him.

'I went up there one day and he says, Boy! he said, You know I got up this morning about two or three o'clock and I was tired of this bed and I just walked downtown. See he still didn't know his leg was off. And he said, You know they had to come down there and *get* me! He said, They went down there and hunted me up and brought me back here and *tied* me to this bed. He'd talk real crazy.

'He kept reaching around and feeling his *spine*, you know how knotty it is, and he'd say, You just feel back there where they cut me open up and down my back. I said, Horace, they didn't operate on your back! That's your *backbone*! I'd say something like that to him and he'd just say, Oh.

'Wendell was there and he'd talk to him every day. He never did know Wendell had been there. H.N., his cousin, an older man, come up there to see him. He never did know that H.N. had been there. His sister and her husband come, he didn't remember it.'

'When did he know his leg was off?'

'Well, they told him. They just went in there one day and told him about his leg being off but the next day he didn't remember it. He wasn't himself to know.

'Well, he stayed in there quite a long time. You see, one thing was, he had to learn to walk. They had two kinds of artificial legs. One was lightweight, made out of aluminum, you know. It was a newer model and much easier to manage, but no, he wouldn't have it. He had to have one of those old-fashioned kind that's carved to look like a leg. Weighed thirty or forty pounds.

'So of course he couldn't get around with it.

'One day the woman at the hospital called me and she said, I want to know why you haven't come after Mr Lambert! Said, He's sitting out on the front walk in a wheelchair with all of his things packed and out there waiting for you to come and pick him up! To *me*! That was after he'd got that artificial leg and he could walk a little bit. But he was a real case. I didn't dare take him. I said, Well that's just too damned bad! You better go out there and get him and put him back to bed! *Because,* I said, You come right down to it he's not anything to me. He's got family of his own and I don't have anything but a one-bedroom apartment and I don't have *no* way of taking care of him or looking after him and I'm not able to lift him. One thing, it was *blowing a blizzard.* I said, He don't have any business coming out of there!

'So Florence come over. Bert called Florence and she got on a plane and flew over.

'Horace wanted to go back out to that little trailer house of his. But it wasn't self-contained. It didn't have a toilet, no running water.'

'He probably wanted to be independent.'

'Yes, but Jessie there was just no way. So Florence come over. I said, Now Florence, I want to tell you something! Before you take Horace out of that hospital. I do *not* want you to bring him *here*. I said, You fix a place for him and you take him to it. Well, you know what she did? She got me to take her over so she could get his pickup ... that was Sunday... and she went over there and got Horace and she brought him to me *bag* and *baggage*! She just didn't want to clean that trailer! It didn't have as much room in it as one room. She could have gone out there and cleaned it herself but she wanted to get somebody else to clean it.

'Well, that was on Sunday and he set around there and he ranted and cussed and ranted and raved and he run Bert down....'

'Why was he running Bert down?'

'Well, he turned against Bert and me. We was the people that really stuck by him all the time he was in hospital.'

'Why did he turn against you?'

'Well ... he just ... because I didn't come to get him that day for one thing and because Bert didn't come to get him for another one. And I didn't think in his weakened condition that he had any business changing beds as cold as it was. It was in the middle of winter.

'Besides, I wasn't able. I had already fooled with him and all the kinfolks that come to visit him until I was just down. I drawed over six hundred dollars out of the bank while he was in the hospital just to feed the extra company I had. Of course there wasn't a one of them that didn't offer to help with the groceries.

'Anyway, she brought him over to me and I had to make the couch down every night. And he had to pull that heavy old wooden leg off every night to go to bed. Florence got him a two pound coffee can to pee in and the first thing he did was knock it over when he got up in the morning and it spilled all over the rug and the floor. And her and Bud didn't even offer to help clean it up. I had to get down on the floor and scrub it up right in their face.

'So this went on till Thursday and still she wasn't saying nothing about taking him to a place. Thursday morning I got up and I called her into the kitchen ... I hadn't slept all night for dreading it ... and I said, Florence I don't care what you do with your daddy but I want him out of this apartment today. I said, I have done my share for your daddy. And I said, You took his money and spent it ... you see, he had almost three thousand dollars in the safe at the hospital. We all thought he was going to die. So Bert and Florence went in there and talked to him ... told him he ought to sign a paper to let Florence get that money out of there ... so he did. He signed the paper. The next day he didn't even remember it. Florence went in and got that money and she told me, Well, I'm going to go home and pay up all my bills. I said, Florence, for god's sake don't spend that money. I said, Put it in a savings account and hold it! I said, I don't think Horace's going to die, and he's going to need that money. She went home and spent every damned bit of it! When poor old Horace got out ... well, he hadn't got out of the hospital when they let him take a plane up there to spend Christmas with Florence. When he come back he said, I told her if she could just give me a thousand dollars of that money she could keep the rest ... and said, You know, she couldn't even do *that*!'

'That's a shocker.'

'Oh, that just turned me against Florence!

'So I said, You taken your daddy's money and spent it and if he don't have the money for a place to stay well you get him on a plane and you take him home with you. I said, He's not my responsibility. I want him out of here and I want it done today. So she got up and went over and got somebody to clean up that little trailer and she put him in it and went and got him some groceries and a few other things and went off and left him there.'

'When did Bud get him?'

'Bud got him ... oh, it wasn't long after that. It was just a little while later.'

'Bud really tried to do well by him didn't he?'

'He sure did, honey. He had a *world* of patience with him. But see, Horace had the leg off on this side. I think it was this one. Yes, I'm sure it was. And *then* he had another stroke on *this* side that partially paralyzed him.'

'Good Lord.'

'He was just getting to be ... he was a real mental case and *awfully* handicapped physically. Bud was as good to him as he could be. Hannah even cooked extra stuff ... her and Douglas lived just down the street in that same house they live in now ... she'd cook things that she *knew* he liked, like cornbread and things like that that he'd always liked. She'd take that stuff over there and sweet milk to have with it ... that's what he always ate at home....'

'I remember he used to crumble cold cornbread in a glass of cold milk and eat it with a spoon.'

'He loved that. So she'd bake and she'd cook things and take them up there and the minute she'd walk in through that door he'd just start cussin her and calling her an old bitch and everything else.'

'Why did he do that?'

'Because he just ... honey, he was crazy. He just had it in for everybody.'

'He didn't have much of a life by then. I guess he just hated anybody that still had a life.'

'I said, *Never* again would I pray for anybody to live except if it's the Lord's will and if it's for the best. Because I got the elders to come up there and pray for him and give him a blessing. The doctors would say, I don't know *what* on *earth* is holding that man here! He should have been dead *days* ago! He don't have a thing going for him and he's got *everything* against him. And he suffered the agonies of the damned.'

'He was always such a quiet man. I tended to feel sorry for him.'

'Honey, I tell you Horace was sort of mean down underneath. He used to accuse Hannah of messing around with men. He hit her one time in the face and busted her nose all to pieces. That was when you was a little girl. She had to go to the doctor and get her nose fixed. Then she'd have to go back to him. She got a little hat with a veil across here to hide her black eyes and her broke nose. Well, that's what caused her to finally leave him. She stopped loving him then.'

'How long did he stay with Bud?'

'Oh, a year or more. And Bud was just so good to him ... you know, and sweet and kind ... he'd come home from work every afternoon to take his daddy for a walk. Get him by the arm and help him. And he'd talk to him in just the gentlest voice.

'Well, they had all these guns around. You remember him and Bud was always fooling around with guns. And he started keeping one of them guns alongside him all the time. He wouldn't lie down on the couch without that gun alongside him. Scared Hannah to death.

'One day the girl was over there cleaning up the house and Horace was fooling with that gun. He got up and come into the kitchen and he dropped that gun on the floor.

'He asked her to hand it to him so she picked it up and handed it to him. Then he asked her to help him get down the steps into the back yard. And she did.

'And he just walked out there and set down in a chair that was there and just put that gun to his head and blowed his brains out.'

I knew yawl ...

'I *knew* yawl'd like peas and cornbread for supper! Douglas said if you're going to do a lot of cooking why don'tcha make a roast or a chicken or something like that. But I said I'll bet you that Mae and Jessie can't get fresh black-eyed peas. I said I'm going to cook peas and cornbread and have fresh butter.'

'Well, it's really good.'

'I love it.'

'Would anybody like a slice of raw onion?'

'Yeah. Me.'

'I can't eat raw onion. I'd love to but it'd tear me up. I'd be sick for the next two days.'

'Well, Mae, how's your throat?'

'The first operation it was better. The doctor said it was blocking up my breathing, all that growth. He said, You're going to feel like a new woman when you start getting your fair share of oxygen. And it was true. I just felt half-drunk. You know how you feel when they give you pure oxygen? Well, after the first operation it was like the air I breathed was pure oxygen. But the second operation has really set me back. I feel worse now than I did before I had the first one.'

'Are you supposed to talk?'

'Listen, you know how *they* are! Let a doctor boss you and you're as good as buried. They want you to stop anything and *everything*! Dr Macauley heard him tell me not to talk and not to smoke and I guess he saw the look on my face. He just went to laughing. He said to Dr Dillon, that was the other doctor, he said, Don't you have anything better to do with your time than stand there and pound your head on the wall?'

'Well, isn't this trip hard on you?'

'Jessie's doing most of the driving. If I get sick we'll just head home.'

'Where yawl going from here?'

'I thought we'd just go straight over to Abilene. I want to be sure to see mama and that way if I get sick I'll have done that much.'

'Jessie, Bud's really anxious to see you. And wait'll you see those little old kids. How long's it been since you saw Danny and Darlene?'

'They were real little.'

Are you my aunt ...

'Are you my *aunt* or my *cousin* or what?'

'I guess we're cousins. I'm your daddy's cousin.'

'Jessie's the one that knows all about poems, Darlene. Why don't you get your poem and read it for her. Darlene wrote a poem at school today.'

'Well, it's just a little one. The teacher said it was really nice.' The slim child thumbed through an assortment of papers, then stood straight, holding one. She had short dark hair cut close to her head and enormous eyes.

'May you be happy,' she read in a clear high voice, 'And live a good life Find a good husband And be a good wife.'

We were living ...

We were living in New Mexico when Bud and I were kids together. When I went back there a couple of months ago I saw an article in the newspaper deploring the state of the poor deprived children who couldn't afford to get into the municipal swimming pool and were reduced to swimming in the irrigation ditches. The sense of it was that charitable organizations should provide free tickets. Another instance of bureaucratic nose-poking. Anybody who'd swap a deep ditch with the water moving in it for a cement pool with chlorine is some kind of a fool. Well, a *usual* kind of a fool.

The ditch Bud and I swam in was a five-minute walk down the dirt road and a turn right for about another five minutes, along the ridged dirt that made the bank. The moisture rose up into the air, softening it, and there was a constant warm smell of mud and weeds gone rampant, the smell of chlorophyll.

The 'flume' was a wooden chute, about three feet wide with sides about two feet high that carried water from a higher ditch and dumped it into ours. Where the water fell a deeper hole had been dug and the ditch widened into a larger pool. The chute was angled about twenty degrees and had slick green moss growing along the bottom. We could go to the top and climb in, sit down, turn loose of the sides and get rushed along, as good as a roller coaster, propelled by foot-deep water, to the end where we dropped about six feet into the ditch and were rolled and tumbled back up to the surface usually about ten or fifteen feet farther down.

'I was sorry to hear about your daddy,' I told Bud. Grown up now with a small moustache.

He looked at me intently for an instant, then ducked his head in a way he always had to keep his feelings in.

'Yeah. I guess it couldn't be helped.'

Mama, show Billie-Jean how...

'Mama, show Billie-Jean how you can sit on your hair.'

'Mama, let me brush your hair.'

Until my grandmother was an old woman she pulled her hair into a bun at the back of her neck. At night when she let it down it fell to her knees. Her daughters were always after her to let them brush it. They took it as a personal treasure. And one of the things she hated most in the world was to have her hair messed with. She was tender-headed but she was also tender-hearted and she'd sit with her teeth gritted after the tangles were out and let one or another of her girls brush the hair that at first was raven black, then salt and pepper, then gray; and by the time it was gray it was me.... 'Grandmama let me brush your hair.' And when she couldn't stand it a moment longer she'd snap, 'That's enough now!' and take the hairbrush ... and as quickly she'd smile and be her own gentle self, the snap being a reflex and not anger. It was always a gift to brush her hair.

She was a scant five feet tall and worked as hard as a full-sized man. Especially after she married her second husband who lost everything that came to his hand. He had red hair and a mean disposition.

In Texas when you say of somebody 'He married a red-headed woman,' or, 'She married a red-headed man,' you're saying Lookout! Maybe nobody says it when the red-head's a gentle one and that's the discrimination. Maybe that phrase itself is a kind of word for red-heads who are bad tempered. Whatever. The fact is: the second time around my grandmama married a red-headed man who was as sour as she was sweet. It must have been a surprise to her. Her first husband, Mr Chapman, had been a good husband, a good father and a frugal man.

'The first thing us kids learned about the old man was not to walk in kicking distance,' my mother said.

There were thirteen kids in all lumping together the ones my grand-mother had by Mr Chapman, the ones the old man had by his first wife and the ones they had together. At least the old man didn't show any preference for his own. He was as bad as he could be to all of them.

My mother stood up to him when she was twelve. She was a sub-stantial twelve-year-old. The old man had Ada in the kitchen and was mad at her about something. Ada was the first child he had with my grandmother ... a sad scrawny thing all her life ... she ended up married to a squint-eyed mechanic named Steve who took up where the old man left off. Anyway, 'He was hitting her with his fists just like she was a man.' She must have been about eight; and my mother picked up a piece of stove wood and said, 'You old son-of-a-bitch you hit her again I'll kill you!' And he laid off.

I meant to talk about my grandmother but it's hard to avoid the old man. By the time I really remember him he had taken to his bed to die.

He was about twenty years older than my grandmother. She was in her twenties when they married. I must have been born when he was around sixty and he went to bed when he was sixty-three. He didn't pass away until he was in his nineties so there was some small margin of error there, which nonplussed him not at all. He had a running, full-scale deathbed scene for more than thirty years.

My mother and her sisters would go to Abilene for a visit and would invite Grandmama to come home with them for awhile. There were always other people in the house who could tend to the old man.

She'd say, 'Well ... Papa *has* been feeling a little better lately. I'll go ask him.'

There'd be a roar from the next room.

'You're doing what no woman has ever done!' he'd yell. 'You're leaving your husband on his deathbed. You go right ahead but know that I won't be here when you get back!' That was his constant theme ... for thirty years. And Grandmother would come back to say, 'Papa isn't really feeling well enough for me to go, honey.'

My memory of him is mostly that if he wanted anything he'd start swearing at the top of his lungs and my Grandmother would rush to him saying, 'Yes, Papa?'

He wore long-handled underwear for pajamas and at times he would undertake a minor trip away from his bed. I remember there would be big pooches like air bubbles in the long-handles at his knees and elbows and seat. He'd stomp to the bathroom or the kitchen glaring and swearing at anyone he met. There was always a sense of scurrying when the old man moved around. Everybody getting out from under foot.

Apart from the scene in the kitchen he only got his come-uppance three times that I know of:

The Ku Klux Klan got after him one year when he had made a crop and had money in the bank and was sending my Uncle Peter to school barefoot after the snows had started. One morning there was a note on the kitchen screen door: 'Get your boy some shoes. KKK.' He paid no attention and three days later a note on the door said, 'We're coming for you tonight. KKK.' And he took Peter into town and bought him some new shoes.

The second time was: In Texas in the summertime when it's really hot the practice on farms is to pull the metal bedsteads out of the house and set them up under trees or on the side of the house opposite to where the sun rises; and everybody sleeps out. Well, the old man always woke up before anybody and he always took it personally that the others were still lying there after he slung his legs over the side of the bed. So he woke them by swearing at them. There was a time when he was making Ada his particular scapegoat and he'd jump her every morning. My mother had taken Ada on as her special charge and one night she told her, 'Tomorrow morning when the old man starts swearing at you tell him to go to hell and take out across the sticker patch. I'll bring you something to eat in the orchard.'

I want to describe a sticker patch for anybody who's never seen one. In some parts of the Texas plains the stickers are the only green things in sight. They flourish no matter what. They lay out huge and uneven and absolute. It's possible for kids who go barefoot to memorize their local sticker patches like a geographer memorizes maps. It saves time to be able to traverse a sticker patch's bald spots instead of having to go around it.

The next morning in grey dawn the old man started raking the air with his daily message and Ada swung her own skinny kid legs over the bed, mumbled, 'Go to hell,' and set out running with the old man hard on her heels. She hit the sticker patch and immediately shifted into an intricate series of little hops and jumps like Little Liza across the ice. The old man hit the sticker patch right after her. His momentum overrode his tender feet and carried him five or six or ten feet into it before he was stopped. Like a cripple, a different man, he turned to start the long hobbling way back, picking his step by step, walking on the sides of his feet.

My mother took Ada some cold biscuits and preserves to the orchard, and Ada came home for supper, coming in quietly to take her place. The old man didn't say a word.

The third time was, he did finally die. Most of his 'mourners' had tight pursed lips while the preacher talked about his virtues.

But my grandmother really cried. She really had loved that mean old fool.

... providing for their own family ...

'... providing for their own family, you know. They didn't have to think of much money because there wasn't a lot of stuff to do and a family's main concern was raising enough foodstuff during the growing season to support them until the next growing season.

'Everybody knew how to cure their own hams and bacon and put up their own sausages and can their vegetables and kill and dress out their own beef. Had their own eggs and chickens and milk, butter, and about the only thing they'd have to bother with would be sugar and coffee and flour.

'We always grew a big corn crop. After the ears dried we'd take the husks off and stack it in the corn crib ... take it easy, babe. You're letting the speedometer creep up. I don't know *why* Buick stopped putting those beepers on the speedometer! You could set them, you know, at the speed you didn't want to go over and they'd make a real racket.'

'I don't need a beeper, Mama. I've got you.'

'Well ... anyway, when we wanted cornmeal we'd get out and work the corn off those ears, rubbing them against an old rub board, and put it in baskets. Then my stepdaddy would take it to the corn mill. They'd stone-grind it. Then they'd bring it back. Mama would sift it. The fine stuff that would go through the sifter she kept to make bread with and the coarse stuff that wouldn't go through the sifter, well, that went to the chickens and pigs.

'That was the best cornmeal you ever ate! It just made the *best* cornbread!

'Another thing we used to do, we had a rub board that the boys had put nails through from the back side so it made a real rough surface, a kind of grater, and before the corn got too hard and dry we'd rub ears over that grater. Then you'd have to sift it. When you did it that way you saved the price of the mill but you got a lot more big rough pieces in it. But none of it was ever wasted because it went to the pigs and chickens. People didn't waste anything! Everything was put to good use.

'There was lots of neighbours. Of course, they lived quite a way apart from one farm to the next. Everybody had cattle and calves growing up. The neighbours would all take turns butchering a beef. The men would divide it up equally between so-many families because there was no way of keeping it. In the wintertime you could keep it. But in the summertime if you'd get hungry for fresh beef ... they'd kill one at our place and butcher it out. Then the next week they'd kill one at the next place. It was so much better than the meat you get now! It was so good.

'Then every winter we'd put up two or three hogs.'

'I thought that after grandmama and the old man got married that he wasted that farm of hers. I thought you never had that place long after they got married.'

'No, I think that Mama ... my mother wasn't a good manager, honey. As Mama said, she was raised up to sit on a silk pillow and sew a fine seam. The phrase had a ritual cadence.

'How was that? You mean her family was better off or something?'

'Well, you see ... she was raised by an old aunt ... whatever she called her. I can't remember her name. And they had plenty.

'She taught Mama how to do fine sewing. Hand-sewing because they didn't have any sewing machines. Everything was made by hand.

'In fact they even took the cotton and carded it. Have you ever seen a cotton carder? They would card this cotton and then they'd get it to rolling in long strings and they'd keep spinning it out some way until it made a thread.

'Then they'd weave their own material and they'd cut those materials to make whatever by hand. Even the men's suits and their own petticoats and dresses and all that.

'Mama knew how to do all that. My mother said that when she got married she had ten quilts that she had pieced and quilted as well as all her own linens and things.'

When Mama had pelligrisy...

'When Mama had pelligrisy we put hoops on over the wagon bed and stretched cloth over them and set out to go to east Texas where there was supposed to be an old nigger man could cure it.

'He had all these little cabins in the woods and the people that come to be cured lived in the cabins. Every morning and every evening he boiled up a mess of what looked like weeds that he gathered in a big old cast-iron pot and everybody that was there had to drink a glass of it. Even the ones that wasn't sick had to drink a glass of it. Us kids really hated it.

'We stayed there about a month and then we started home when Mama got better.

'Well, one evening just at dark we come to an old house beside the road. There wasn't nobody lived there and we thought to spend the night there under a roof for a treat.

'We brought the broom in and swept out a couple of the rooms and we made down pallets and we all went to bed.

'Well, the room Mama and the old man were in had an old wood stove against one of the walls. Mama woke out of a sound sleep hearing that stove rattle. Then she heard footsteps going across the floor and out of the room. She called out to Ernie, he used to sleepwalk when he was a boy, but there wasn't no answer. The footsteps just went on back into the other room and then they stopped so she figured he was back on his pallet and she started to go back to sleep.

'Then the footsteps come back into the room and she heard them cross the floor again back to the old wood stove, and she could hear like he was climbing onto that old wood stove. She was worried that he was going to get hurt so she struck a match and lit a candle but there wasn't anybody there. Nobody on the stove, nobody in the room at all, just the old man asleep. So she got up and went to look at the kids and they were all asleep too.

'She went back to her own place and laid down and as soon as she blew the candle out somebody jumped down off the stove in the dark and went walking across the floor and out of the room.

'Well, there wasn't nobody else heard it but Mama didn't get to sleep all night for those footsteps crossing the room and climbing onto that old stove and jumping down and walking back across the room.

'She knew she wasn't dreaming and that it had to be her second-sight so she just resigned herself to it and laid there listening.

'The next day we learned down the road that a man had killed his wife in that house nearly twenty years before and he stood on that

44

stove to hoist her body into the space over the ceiling boards to hide it.'

When my father died ...

'When my father died ... see, he broke with his family before he ever met my mother ... and he never went back except for his parents' funeral. And when he died there was a write-up in the paper said he was from one of the most prominent families in this big county that he come from. So you know they were bound ... they wouldn't say that if they didn't have a lot of property and stuff. Well, us kids should get our daddy's part of that stuff and over all these years it would be increasing, you know.

'I think they tend to have a statute of limitations on that, Mama.'

'Well, they may do it but under the circumstances that they wasn't any notification of *any* kind or no provision of *any* kind that we know of we still might be able to do something about it.

'And Emmett went back there one time and he come back and said You ought to go back east and visit some of your relatives, he said, They're *all* wealthy and they're all lawyers and doctors and writers and artists and ... all of that, you know.'

'How long was he there? How did he meet them? I mean ... you don't even know who your relatives are in the east do you?'

'Well no ... I mean it's back in east Texas somewhere ... or back in the east ... he said *east*. I just wish Mama would write to him before she dies and get the name of the county at least where my daddy was born and raised ... And if I could get the name of that county I could get old John Henry Fisher to get on it and tell him I'd give him a certain percent of whatever came out of it....'

(a long pause for the contemplation of advantage)

'Yeah, we've got too much air in the tires. Are you getting tired?'

45

A letter to My Grandaughter

Dear Jessie I am thinking to day of you when you were the very sweetest of little girls. Your Mama was working and you were staying with me. And I thought of how much we loved you. So much your Aunt Louella who was just a little bit older than you prayed for your Mother to die so we could keep you Thank the good Lord he knew and had a better answer to that prayer.

You wanted to know a few things about my life. I can assure you dear it has been quite different to yours. My Mother died when I was 2 years old. My father remarried when I was 5 years old and lived just 1 year after his marriage. 2 months after his death my Step Mother gave birth to a little baby boy and she died with Pneumonia. When the baby was 1 month old the baby's Uncle my Step Mother's brother got homes for the baby and me. My little half brother was killed in the 1st World War in France 3 days before the War ended.

I can remember a few little interesting events that happened during my Step Mother's life time. We lived close to a big creek. My Step Mother decided one day she would take my little Step Brother and me and go visiting. We had to go through this creek bottom. On the way back home we were attacked by a bunch of wild hogs. Some one had cut down a tree. It was bent over. My Step Mother threw us children up in the tree and climbed up into it herself. I can imagine how worried my Father must have been about us. I had a wonderful Father dear. I know that by what people has told me about him. Everybody that knew him loved him and I loved him dearly. I remember he bought my Step Mother a big yellow turkey gobbler. She was real proud of it because of the colour. There were lots of wild turkeys them days and Father wanted to go out and kill one and he wanted to take her gobbler and stake him and he would gobble and the turkeys would come to him. Well she didn't want him to but he promised her he would be careful but he killed the wild turkey and Mothers yellow gobbler too and she cried about it.

In my new house I don't think I was ever really happy or unhappy. I went to school for 4 years just long enough to learn to read and write and arithmatic as the old tune goes played to the tune of a Hickory stick. Which was used very often. Not in school but at home. The people I lived with sure believed in using the rod but love they knew nothing about. If they loved or cared for me they never let me know. Once I started to the well for a bucket of water. Mr Womack had a big

46

dog. He was standing on the steps in front of me. I just kinda kicked him out of my way. He threatened to give me a whipping for that. 2 boys he had hired called the dog off to the field and shot him. He never did know what happened to the dog. I didn't either until I married one of the boys and he told me.

That was my first husband. I was 14 years old the 25th of December. We were married the 25th of July 1896. Eunice our first baby was born 16 June 1897. Our second baby was born August 27th 1900 just 2 weeks before the great Galveston Flood. My 3rd baby a little boy was born the 3rd day of August in 1902. On December 3rd 1902 my baby died. On the day my baby died his Father was seriously ill with Pneumonia and died on Sunday which was 3 days later.

I went then with my 2 little girls and lived with their Grandmother and Grandfather until I married your Grandfather Peter Joseph Chapman in 1904. We had 5 children. Lost one little baby girl when she was 12 days old. We had 1 boy and 3 little girls your Uncle Peter and Aunt Ethel and Aunt Hannah and your Mother who was 7 months old when her Father died in April 1913 with cancer of the stomach in Willis Montgomery County Texas.

I left there and taken the children and went back to Mitchell County and lived with them. Most of the time with your Aunt Bertha and her husband Will Gatliff who was real kind to me and the children.

I stayed there until I married Mr Ingram in Oct. 1st 1914 in Colorado City Texas. We had 5 children 2 boys and 3 girls. Lost both our boys. That left me 7 children out of the 13.

So you see darling there hasn't been too much happiness mixed up in my life but I am not complaining. I have been blessed in so many ways.

As you know, Mr Ingram died in 1953.

My children and grandchildren have been such a comfort and blessing to me. If I make no mistake I have 7 children 21 grandchildren 31 Great Grandchildren 2 Great Great Grandbabys, expecting another one in December. That will be Jimmy's baby. I may never see them but I am proud of them. I have 2 new Great grandsons. One will be 2 weeks old next Monday and one will be 2 weeks old next Saturday. Of course dear this isn't old stuff but I thought maybe you would like a little of the new along with the old.

Talking about old stuff I wonder if you can imagine pretty print material selling for 1 ct a yard. I can remember when we sold butter for

47

5 cts a lb and thought we were getting a good price for it. We had an old fashioned wooden churn and a churn Dasher. The lid that fit on the churn had a hole in the centre. You put the handle of the dasher through that. Sometimes we would have to churn for hours before the cream would turn to butter but Oh what good butter and buttermilk we had. But you would really get tired churning.

Your Grandfather fixed me a milkbox. We had a windmill and a wonderful well of water. He bored a hole in each end of this box and put a pipe in each hole. We let the windmill run all the time and that cold water was running through this box all the time ... I kept the milk jars and butter bowls wrapped in cloth and the milk and butter was just as cold as the water. And we really enjoyed it. We also irrigated a garden from the well. We had a beautiful garden out by the well and most all kinds of vegetables. I went to the garden the day your Uncle Peter was 2 weeks old to gather vegetables for dinner, had on a loose dress with just a yoke in it and it just hung loose from this yoke. Had a pan of vegetables gathered and when I stooped down to pick it up there was a big tarantula half out and half in the yoke of this dress. That is half of it was in between my dress and slip and the other half outside. So I didn't pick up the pan. I just left it and caught my dress and slip up on each side of the thing and held it out away from me until I got back to the house and the dining table. My oldest daughter was in the kitchen. I just eased the whole mess on the table. She picked up a stick of wood and put it on it and mashed it. I unfastened my dress and it fell out on the table. I know the Lord was certainly with me in that deal to keep me from being scared so bad and to be composed enough not to start fighting at it. If I had it would have run back in my clothes and would have bitten me. As it was it never moved or changed position. I really think dear I do have a Guardian Angel that watches over me. Once when I was little it was coming up a cloud fixing to rain. Mr Womack had bundled a lot of fodder in the field and if it rained on it it would ruin it so he wanted Aunt Nannie and me to go and help him put it in the wagon so he could haul it in before it got wet. We were gathering it up in our arms. I felt something wriggling next to my body and I held the bundle out from me and a grown rattlesnake fell to the ground. I had picked it up with the bundle of fodder.

A few funny little things happened. Once I had gone across the field to visit a little neighbour girl. On the way back home I had to pass some cows. There was one in the bunch that would fight but I thought maybe she wouldn't notice me but I was mistaken. I had passed her just a little way when she spied me and here she come. There was a little creek between me and the corral fence. When I got to that creek I was sure she was going to catch me. I let out a pretty loud scream and it scared the cow and she dug the ground up a good little ways trying to stop. I had a real hearty laugh about it all when I got over my scare.

Well dear, I guess that is about all. Of course there were a lot of things that happened I guess that I don't remember but I guess this is about all you care to read. Hope it isn't too boring.

Your grandmother who loves you very much.

The houses where my grandmother ...

The houses where my grandmother and the old man lived when I was little were various but the same, one storey high, weathered and tired, used up. What paint still clung was only a further complication of the rotting wood.

There was usually a sagging wooden porch for taking the evening air after supper and a rocking chair for grandmama and the babies.

She would start with the youngest and rock it to sleep, then she'd carry it to bed. She'd rock and sing, cradling the children against her, moving up the line through the older ones until there would be a rebel who could stop it all by declaring fiercely, 'I'm too *old* to be rocked to sleep!'

Inside those houses there would be a smell throughout of too many lives, as if animals lived in the walls. A memory smell that stayed into present time as a woman's hair will take the smell of frying onions while her hands still smell of the fresh onions she sliced to be fried.

Oilcloth covered the table, flowers or checks, cracked and worn thru to the fabric, the pattern spoiled by the overwhelming pattern of wear. On the floor the linoleum had been used into islands of patternless brown at the sink, the stove, around the table.

The kitchen chairs were wired together, some became stools with a row of broken bits along one edge like teeth to show where the back had been. Straw chairs burst through underneath to remain a static explosion, fixed, under the board that was laid across to be sat on.

The corrosion of time is accelerated by poverty. Things grow old faster. Cheap dresses hung unevenly from their first washing. Plastic buttons melt against the iron. Cheap bright colours fade and run. Cheap shoes begin to curl up at the toes the first wearing, reaching for that foetal position old shoes take when they die. The shoestrings break, are taken out, knotted, returned to the shoe a blot marring the clear x's.

All the rooms except the kitchen held beds, iron and brass bedsteads that moved from house to house with mattresses made of feathers or of stuffed cotton turned hard as rock.

All the appurtenances, called by name, often travesties of the original intention, were there. The *rug* worn to rags, trails walked through to the floorboards, was there to be swept. A lumpy shape, humps and hollows of displaced batting, springs a threat, was the *couch*, or the *sofa* or even the *davenport*.

And boxes of old clothes, old toys, old objects no one could throw away because there was still some good left in them, the *belongings* were stacked under the beds and along the walls.

The pride and blindness of the poor, their persons as their houses, *worn*, worn down to the thread. Lined hands, lined faces, none of that ease of muscles a little money gives.

In all that grubbiness and unspoken despair the children were the joy. They were fresh however. Their necks were nuzzled, their sides and feet were tickled to make them scream. They slept and waked in poverty's matriarchy. All those daughters, my grandmother's daughters, with husbands who came and went, had babies who came and stayed.

If my grandmother passed her childhood without feeling loved, the children and grandchildren who grew up near her had no such problem.

It was so intimate, ripe with reality.

So what I knew...

So what I knew of those houses where the old man lay always dying was the middle time when they sat between farm country and the town, usually in some old farmhouse that went with nearby land that somebody else was farming. If you haven't seen the place you've seen the pictures.

And by the time my eyes were in my head they were in the houses that they would be in forever, in succession.

The yards for those houses were hard-packed dry dirt where whatever grass that grew was accidental and doomed, a few tall sprigs of dusty green that must finally join the rest; dead roots in hard clay. The only green with any hope, a jagged mixture of rough grass and wild mint, would signal a leaky faucet.

What else was common?

Wrecked cars out back, a woodpile and a raised iron cauldron for making soap out of accumulated fat drippings and lye water from wood ash, a playhouse, its walls outlined by lines of small rocks under a shade tree, a profusion of bent pots and broken crockery and misshapen dolls, their eyes staring.

And Franklin Delano Roosevelt, as absolute as the sun and the moon. It doesn't seem at all political to me that I can't stand to hear a word against him.

His WPA and CCC made the first jobs to be counted on by one whole generation of Texas young men from poor homes.

One of the boys grandmama talks about losing went over a cliff in the back of a CCC truck and was killed.

'Mama knew it the minute it happened. She stopped in the middle of the kitchen floor and started crying and said Joey is laying on the ground. His head's broke open on a rock.' And sure enough we got the telegram the next day.'

She was small and sweet and tough ...

She was small and sweet and tough, moving among the various armed camps of that household. The kids chose up sides daily and stopped just short of killing each other.

As when Peter one day had sharpened his axe and was chopping at whatever caught his eye. Hannah was always a tease and she angled off what she was doing to put her finger down on a good-sized wood chip that Peter was aiming for.

'You better move your finger. I'm getting set to chop that piece of wood.'

'You better not chop this piece of wood because I ain't planning to move my finger off of it.'

They both were truthful.

Hannah didn't move her finger and Peter did chop the wood.

Wills of iron.

Hannah ran to the house screaming with her finger pouring blood and dangling, caught only by a piece of skin.

Grandmama boiled a needle and some thread and sewed the finger on and it took. It had a lump where it had been cut through and Hannah couldn't move it much. Then a couple of years later she got into the bad habit of finger-twisting. She grabbed Mae's hand once to give her a twist and Mae twisted first. Hannah's finger gave a loud crack and swelled up for a week or two and when the swelling went down the lump was only half the size it had been and she could move it a lot more.

Mae took a milk pail once: 'I didn't think of it as *stealing*. It was more like it just didn't seem fair to me that they had all those new pails stacked up and we just had one old bucket. So when I went home I just took a pail along with me. I picked out a good one. But when Mama saw it she went dead quiet and asked me where I got it. Well, I couldn't sit down for a week. And I had to take the pail back. I couldn't even just take it back and sneak it onto the pile. I had to take it back to Mr Holliday and tell him I took it. It was the only time in my life that Mama ever whipped me.'

I remember the two times in my life grandmama ever whipped me.

The first was when my Aunt Louella had climbed onto my mother's bed to play and I got territorial about it. I got a broom and went to work on her. She got tangled in the covers trying to get away and my grandmother found me there pounding on the lump under the covers and screaming, 'This is my Mama's bed!'

The second time was when I was alone in the house and locked grandmama out. She circled the outside of the house as I circled the inside to be standing there solemnly looking out at every door and window as she came to it.

Running Set of Lies

There was a running set of lies that got handed to me all the time I was growing up. Whenever Issue-Number-One came up all the women's faces changed and all the girls were lied to.

I realize it was a *conservative* ... as in *protective* ... device, but at my end of it it added up to a lot of confusion.

For instance, on my fourteenth birthday a boy who was maybe sixteen was going to come to the apartment and formally ask my parents if he could take me on my first official date. They had agreed that he could ask so it seemed likely the answer was yes.

I went to the corner drugstore to hang out with my friends and my mother showed my father some presents I had got that morning one of which was the classic Five Year Diary which, when she laid it down, fell open to what I had immediately written in on receiving it, so as not to forget. The week before in a movie house with my friends I had kissed the boy who was due to arrive around four this afternoon. It was there in black and white with exclamation marks for ecstasy.

That entry proved to be the first and last of that 'diary.' One thousand eight hundred and twenty-four days down the drain, precluded by stupidity.

I had taken the abstraction of *My Diary* as an allowance, proof against getting hoisted on the hook because you wrote it down. The power of a defined occasion. And I learned the way it really was when I got home and faced those two faces. There was no doubt that I had made a mistake.

My mother took me into the kitchen to talk to me.

Kissing in the movies is vulgar.

But worse than that ... and she rang the shift on me ... no girl should kiss a boy until they're engaged.

I couldn't believe it ... that she was saying it. I looked at her and she looked as solemnly back as if she meant to stand by that statement against come what may. I couldn't believe it. I mean ... she came off a *farm*.

And when Aunt Ethel's baby came seven months after she was married it was because she had got tired of carrying it and swallowed a bottle of castor oil.

I mean to say the girls and women were falling left and right and if there wasn't a good cover-up story to preserve the myth ... a bottle of castor oil to produce a fully developed eight pound premature baby ... of course there was acceptable leeway because she *was* married ... then you became an example of life's other side. And the sin was to be that example.

Given some proposal of *winning* you looked around and just saw the losers. I don't doubt it had to do with ... I came from a rockbottom *poor* family that *aspired* to the lower middle class, and most of them made it. Some of them did better. But the time I'm talking about was when they were still talking it up and learning the gestures at the movies and learning what their desires were by window shopping.

It was hopeless. It was truly intellectual. The *ideal* occurred in conversation as the *real*, and what was really happening was shameful, not to be mentioned.

The fear of going lower was the real motive power. And the only *lower* was to be in the same place but disgraced as well. Just a step away. But it loomed downward like something you could avoid and the imagination of it was a misstep would do it.

Or you could jump. You could be finally desperate and jump.

Louella was my mother's youngest half-sister, Grandmama's last baby. 'This is my baby,' she'd say introducing her, even when she was grown. She was about four years older than me so when I was fourteen she was eighteen. We made a summer visit to Abilene that year and I felt awkward and pleased to walk on the street with her, the soldiers whistling and she being so cool, paying no attention.

She was a soft full-bodied beauty with blonde hair pulled up in a '40s Betty Grable pompadour and platform ankle-strap shoes. She was proud of her hands and I thought she was right to be. She had curvaceous fingers with exact long nails. She changed her nail polish every time she changed her lipstick so they would match.

Abilene was packed full of soldiers. There was a rumour for awhile that a black regiment was going to be stationed there and the old man, Louella's father, swore that he was going to buy an acre of land and a shotgun and he meant to shoot any nigger that set foot on his property. He had no notion of patriotism.

It was his usual kind of bad-mouthing. He was on relief and didn't have the hard cash to buy a shotgun shell, much less a shotgun, much less an acre of land.

Louella fell in love with a handsome and sweet-natured Italian from Detroit. They married. Ten months later Louella had twins, a boy and a girl. The boy was dark and larger with black straight hair and (after they changed colour) black eyes. The girl was tiny and blue-eyed with blonde curls. All by the book.

But there was a curve. A month before the babies were born Louella applied for the army's family allotment and learned that it was already being paid out to a wife and two children back in Detroit.

The Italian really loved her, too. He begged her to stay with him and cried. He kept crying and swearing that he'd get a divorce and that all he wanted was Louella.

But her heart was broken.

She had the babies and went on the town. That open. Within two months she was pregnant again and married to a man who turned out to be a forger and went to prison.

It seemed to me then and it seems to me now that I had about as much chance in that economy as a snowball in hell. I had a glamoured mind and I sure did want to be close to somebody.

When I was just turned seventeen I was knocked up by Blacky James in a small town near Lubbock while I was on a visit to my Aunt Hannah. He was a prize-winning diver, a cheer-leader at Texas Tech, and he wanted to be an FBI agent. He wore fancy hand-tooled boots and rode in local rodeos. He was really flashy.

It was like the sky fell in. It was a dimensional change. It was my turn. And I fought it with the slimmest, most ignorant resources. I became a living breathing salvage project. I walked around in a daze with my ears ringing from quinine and my skin parboiled from hot baths. I jumped off every table in sight.

I'd gone back to Albuquerque and it was a coincidence that my mother decided just then to go to Texas for a visit.

I called Blacky's house as soon as I could, but he was back at school.

And the self-preservation scheme went on. On a blazing hot day I went out with a pick-axe to dig a trench in the hard clay back of the garage. It seemed more to the point somehow to make a useless trench than to just dig at random. It gave me a chance to see where I'd been.

As a trench it was pathetic; a foot wide, a foot deep, and as long as it had to be. The clay was as hard as stone. Every inch counted.

At one moment my mother and aunt stood watching me, their eyes like tabulators.

'I'm getting some exercise,' I gasped.

'You better get in the house,' Aunt Hannah said drily, 'you look green.'

Mrs James was an invalid. She spent her time in bed. When she got up it was to clamber creep into a nearby wheelchair. She had dyed red hair and was fat. Her skin was gray white. The small bedroom stank with her smell.

'She knows a good thing when she sees it,' she spat at us, meaning me. 'She had to mess around and now she's got what's coming to her and she thinks she's going to get herself a college boy for its daddy.'

Mr James stood near the head of the bed watching us. He was quiet. It was clear that his wife was the master of the moment.

We had been quiet too. Shamed. We were shamed. But my mother has never passed up an opponent in her life.

'You filthy mouthed old woman. You turn your talk around or I'll haul you out of that bed and climb all over you! I don't care if you are a cripple!'

The upshot was that Blacky was telegraphed to come home.

But of course it amounted to nothing. There was nothing in it to begin with ... not like a place to be.

The three of us drove around in a car to 'talk about it.'

Blacky explained how this would all be a large problem to him. And it was true.

'If you don't want him honey you don't have to have him,' my mother said. 'You know I'd love any baby of yours no matter where it came from.'

To make a long story short I had an abortion. One way out. One way to get on with it.

Almost home free.

I can't think why it's so much like people walking along the highway with their backs to the traffic and high odds against them. And it's the only highway.

Mae, are you feeling good?

'Mae, are you feeling good? I mean ... I know you're not feeling *good* but you think you're recovering and getting over ...?'

'It's real slow.'

'I don't see where they cutcha.'

'They didn't. They went down through my mouth and got it.'

'Thank goodness! I was expecting Mae to have a scar there and one there of some sort.'

'No. They put a ... You know they go down in your throat and work just like the time they had to go up into my kidney. They went up thru my bladder. They've got these little mirrors and these teeny-weensy little lines that they can run down into there. The first one wasn't a bit bad. I mean it took a long time to get over ... but....'

(Crystal brings in iced tea)

'Why didn'tcha just have the *maid* bring those in?'

'She's taking her rest.' (laughing)

'Didja get the house clean enough before she got here this morning to

57

keep from embarrassing her?'

'Naw, I'm not *about* to embarrass *the maid.*'

'Well, Crystal, thank you kindly.'

'Are you going to stand up or are you going to sit down?'

'I'll be back in a minute.'

'Where I'm nursing that old woman she just can't stand it if the house is a mess when the maid comes!'

'You mean you have to straighten up?'

'I keep the part I live in straight.'

'Well, this is the maid's day off so I get to relax today.'

'I told Crystal when we got here this morning I said If I ever look at another man it'll be because he's got money enough to hire me a maid and a cook and a yardman. Because nothing else much interests me....' (laughing)

'I'm telling you the truth ... I've been that way a long time.'

'If I'da been doing the kind of work Ada has been doing I'd of latched onto me a rich man a long time ago.'

'I bet you would've. I've had some chances too, Mae. I've even been told "take that old man" and he died in no time!'

'If you get one with enough money then you could *hire* somebody to come in and look after him!'

'This old man was in a wheelchair and I was nursing his sister. They lived together....'

'Let me tell you one thing before I forget it....'

'He would've married me. He died about thirty days....'

'Fred said something about he was coming home the end of this month. I said, Call me before you do because I'm thinking about running off with the yardman. I have this big fat old guy comes and mows the lawn once a week. Fred just went to laughing. He said, If that's what my baby wants that's what I want her to have. I said, You know how much trouble I give the men. I said, Boy, I don't have no time for 'em. And he said, I realize that, but Boy, I sure did enjoy the little dab of trouble you give me.'

I sat on Grandmama's bed and held her hand. Everybody else was doing the doing. It sounded like they had finally got her where they could take care of her despite herself.

'When Floyd come to visit last week with his twin babies I thought Mama was just going to wear herself out! All she wanted to do was hold those babies. We finally had to just take them away from her. Floyd put them in their little baskets and we put them all the way across the room against the wall. And she still just wouldn't take her eyes off those baskets. The least little sound from one of those babies and she'd raise up and look over to try to see it.'

It was a big old house ...

'It was a big old house and a pretty one but hadn't anybody lived in it as long as we could remember. Us kids wouldn't go anywhere near it. We had to pass it every day when we walked to school but we kept well down into the road when we passed by.

'Well, this day I'm talking about it had been raining and the only way I could keep my shoes out of the mud was to walk high on the slope that ran up toward the old house. I don't know why I was walking by myself. I guess I got kept in after school or something.

'Anyway, there wasn't nobody with me and it was getting near sundown. Well, the closer I come to that old house the slower I walked. I just knew there was going to be something jump out and grab me.

'By the time I got in front of the door I wasn't moving more than an inch in a minute and sure enough that front door that hadn't ever been open was open. Just the screen door was there and I could see right through it.

'Well, at first what I saw I thought it was a little girl. Then I saw it was a woman. Not all of her. It was just a head. It was floating there about three feet off of the floor and it had long yellow hair that fell straight down all the way to the floor and it was looking right back at me through the screen door. I just went on walking like nothing was the matter, looking at it and it looking back until I got past where I could see it. Then I cut and run until I couldn't run no more. I remember everybody was just setting down to supper when I come bolting through the back door shaking all over and white as a sheet.'

... this was up north ...

'... this was up north where the ghost stories really are something ... We were all told to steer clear of this place. It was a big old mansion with stained glass windows. You really could see lights in there at night in some of the rooms. But it was just somebody circulating stories and then using the place for drinks and gambling. That's how most ghost stories go.

'At the same time I'm firmly convinced that there's millions of restless spirits walking this earth.'

'Oh my! I am too. I mean, I have some understanding of it now.'

'I'll say....'

'Jessie, reach up there and turn that light on. Turn it so it comes on this side. Or somewhere where it won't be in her face. That'll be alright.'

Them two little girls ...

'Them two little girls was named Cora and Dora. They was twins. They had an older sister ... I don't remember what her name was. That Cablet girl, Mama, that had the baby....

'Miz Cablet would come down and she'd *talk* to Mama. She'd act so mournful and so sad, and I finally caught on that it was this oldest girl she was talking about. Finally this girl had a baby.

'Well, all this Miz Cablet would do would be to treat that girl like she was dirt. She turned Mama against her. She turned us kids against her.

'I told Mama, I said, Mama, I think that's real mean of Miz Cablet to talk that way about her daughter. I said, I want to go down there and see that baby!

'Mama said it was alright. So Hannah and me went down there and here Cora and Dora was flitting around, you know. And the mother was acting like she had a leper in her house. She was setting, the daughter, was setting over in the corner in an old-fashioned rocker with that tiny little baby. She just had her head bowed over it like this, you know. She didn't even raise up her head when we come in.

'I went over and I told her, I said, We've come down here to see your little baby. And she looked like she was so happy.

'It was the cutest little baby. I never could stand that woman after that.'

The first book ...

'The first book he wrote was "Chasing the Wild Asparagus."'
  'Who wrote?'
  'Euell Gibbons.'
  'That's what made him famous.'
  'He didn't have any education. He just got out and went to scouting and snooping about these wild foods. He's wrote about four books now.'
  'You know that joke that ends up "you ever *shit* a pine tree?"'

... what we did to the old man ...

'... what we did to the old man, he was real skittish and he'd hooked up a thing out at the henhouse so if anybody went in there....'
  'It'd rattle a can in the house.'
  'Yeah. So he rigged it up and two or three days went by without nothing rattling out there and us kids was getting restless about it. So we hooked up to his hookup. He'd just doze off to sleep and we'd pull our string. It'd sound like the damn roof was falling in! We had him jumping and running for three or four nights in a row. Finally I got started laughing and couldn't stop and give it all away. He come in mad as hell after his latest trip out the the henhouse and as soon as he saw me laughing he guessed it. He yelled, What are you damned kids up to now!'

The old man used to wake up ...

'The old man used to wake up in the middle of the night and think he couldn't breathe. He used to have the idea that at night all the oxygen in the room would get used up and he was going to die in his sleep. Anyway, he used to wake up and just run snorting for the window and throw it up and stick his head out and take big breaths, like he'd just come up out from under the water.

'Well, this one night he woke up almost too late, that is, he didn't think he could make it to the window. So he reached down and grabbed up one of his shoes and heaved it toward the window. There was all the crash of the glass breaking and he figured he'd saved his life. But the next morning he saw that he'd broke the mirror over the chest of drawers.

'Another thing, you know how he used to shove Vix up his nose? When he had a cold he'd rub Vix all over his chest and on his temples, and then for good measure he'd stuff it up his nose and swallow some as well.

'Well, one night he woke up with a cold and he headed for the drawer where the Vix was kept and he went through that whole routine. But the next morning he found out that he'd used a jar of white shoe polish.'

Mae, not to change ...

'Mae, not to change the subject but you look good.'
　'She looked awful tired last night.'
　'How'd you like me to prepare the liver?'
　'Do you pound liver?'
　'I'll tell you how I prepare it and you can do it any way you want to. I turn it in flour ...'
　'Yeah, Mama likes it that way and cooked brown.'
　'Turn it in flour that has salt and pepper in it.'
　'Then put gravy on it and let it simmer.'
　'If you turn it in flour and fry it brown and pour the grease off. Then put just a little water in the pan and put a lid on....'
　'I don't put *any* water in it at all. I just fry it *really* slow for a long time and it comes out fried real crisp. Then if you want gravy you can make it in the pan afterwards.'
　'I start the grease and fry the onions until they're absolutely brown. So the whole pan has that taste of brown onions. Then I take the onions out to the side. Then I turn the liver in flour and lay it in the pan and put it on a low fire and just cook it for a long time.'
　'On a low fire?'
　'So it comes out really brown.'
　'Hannah cooked some at the house one time. It really amazed me. She put the liver in there and she braised it very lightly. It wasn't even tan. Just enough to set the flour. Then she put the onions she cut up into the pan on the range. And she added *milk.*'
　'Well, then you're going to end up with stewed onions.'
　'That's exactly what happened.'
　'That's the way I fix it *except* I take the liver and salt and pepper it and turn it in flour. Then I put it in hot grease and I brown it real good. Then I pour off every drop of that grease and I put some water in the bottom of the pan. I slice my onions thick and lay them all over the top and I put a lid on it and I turn it low.'
　'I can't get onions to come out right unless I cook them first.'
　'... so when I get through I have my onions *and* gravy *and* liver ...'
　'I cook 'em in separate pans a lot of times you know.'
　'I've tried making liver and onions like that, you know, like Papa used to eat. He'd have the gravy and all just gooey. You could actually take the onions off the top and have the liver and gravy on the bottom.'

You know how...

'You know how Louella's husband is about Sally.'

'I don't appreciate that type.'

'Who is that?'

'Louella's husband. He *acts* like a prude.'

'He says, I have to keep an eye on Sally. She's the sexiest little bitch I ever saw in my life. Not that *I'd* touch her, mind you! I told Louella, I said, You better *watch* him!'

'Yes, she had.'

'Damned well better.'

'He looks at her just like she was a *bowl* of something *good* to eat!'

'She is beautiful and I'm not kidding you. She's got that long dark hair.'

'I guess I never saw her.'

'She's Louella's youngest.'

'Peter's got the worst crush on her you ever heard of!'

'Well, any man would. Just to look at her.'

'She was a lovely little girl. I saw her a couple of years ago and she was a little doll then.'

And my grandmother says from the bed, 'Well, she's a grown girl now.'

Let's see ...

'Let's see ... She's in Root isn't she?'
  'I should have called her back yesterday.'
  'Why dontcha just set down here ...'
  'Is that light too bright for you, grandmama?'
  'In Root for the Ethel Leary residence ...'
  'Root. Ethel Leary. You don't have it? Alright, let's have that. Slow down. What was it? 2472 ...? Operator? Well, she's gone. We'll just try this and if it ain't the number we'll just call the operator and say that Information gave us the wrong number. She was in just too damned big of a hurry!, (dialing)
  'Are yawl ready for your lunch now?'
  'Lord, no!'
  'I should've called Ethel back yesterday it only cost half as much ... Howdy! This is your sister ... you know the squeaky one ...! Oh well, thank you ... I'm not back to normal but my voice is a little bit better ... Are you going to be home today ...? Well, no ... you go ahead and we'll come over tonight. What time will you be home ...? Naw, we'll just go over to Velma's and visit with her awhile and give you a ring later ... Oh, sure enough ...? No, you go ahead and go. We'll just wait till later and drive over. We'll be there when you get home ... No. Don't do that. Somebody might go in there and get something ... We'll just ... are you going to Lubbock? Well, here, say hello to Mama and we'll see you sometime this evening ... O.K. Here's Mama.'
  ('She said we better not go over to Velma's until we've had a chance to talk to her. She says Velma stays awake all night and sleeps all day and's under the care of her psychiatrist.')

'Grandmama, I'll try to get back to see you again.'
  'Honey, I'll try to stay alive long enough for it.'

You know, Crystal

'You know, Crystal has a very different sense of the old man than yawl had. Her sense of him is that he did a lot more joking and he wasn't as mean.'

'Well, he *would* get jolly if the house was filled with *his* relatives and Mama was in the kitchen filling a fourteen-foot or sixteen-foot-long table with baked turkeys and baked chickens and cakes and pies and things like that for Christmas dinner.

'I remember one Christmas ... we had this long long table with benches on the sides for the kids and then a chair at each end for him and for Mama. One Christmas I remember counting twenty-six of his relatives that was there. Mama had been cooking for a week. We had our own turkeys and our own chickens, our own beef and our own eggs, butter and milk, all that stuff. Mama had baked cakes and pies all over the place and a turkey and a couple of hens besides all the vegetables and stuff she fixed.

'You know how kids are. I couldn't hardly wait until we got ready to eat. Of course, the grown-ups always ate first then the children ate later.

'It was always *my* sense of things to feed the children first and then the grownups.

'Anyhow, I couldn't wait till the food was on the table. I'd already picked out just what I was going to have ... a great big drumstick from the turkey and some dressing, mashed potatoes and green beans and cranberry sauce. Then I was going to have a couple of kinds of pie, and so forth. I had it all figured out.

'Then my stepdad took my plate. He just without a by your leave picked up my plate and started putting food on it. I said, That is *not* what I want! I want so-and-so ... So to play Mr Big he had me get under the table and stay there until everybody had finished their Christmas dinner. Then I got the leavings.

'So you see Crystal got one sense of him and we've got another one. Her view has softened over the years since he died and mine hasn't.'

'She was younger.'

'She was just a baby at that time. She was ten years younger'n me. And he was her father. I guess that did make a difference.

'She was a lot like him, you know ... but I'm sure....

'He *was* a very talented old man. He would have made a good musician or something. He played a violin beautifully without ever having had a lesson of any kind.

'But the things we pulled on him were really something.'

When we were living ...

When we were living in Galveston or San Antone, someplace really hot, there was a lady across the street who had a crazy daughter. She had her living room divided down the middle with floor to ceiling hogwire mesh. Her daughter lived on one side of it and she lived on the other. The radio was on her side and they both had rocking chairs and they'd sit and rock and sew and talk and listen to the radio.

When the daughter was having a good spell her mother would unlock the cage door and they'd sit together in the mother's part of the room rocking and talking. But when visitors came or the girl started to get excited or when she wanted to go outside the mother would put her back and lock the door.

Everyone agreed that the mother had a hard time of it and that it was decent of her to keep the girl at home instead of putting her in the county hospital.

Texas mental institutions were really poor and quite recently I heard a story about one place where the director only has an MA in psychology, he's not even a psychiatrist. And one girl was brought in there in a state of shock because her father raped her, and his way of dealing with it was to hypnotize her and get her to remember it all and she came out of hypnosis screaming, then zapped into rigid catatonia. The implication was, never to come out again.

But you don't know how much to believe of sensational stories.

We used to visit across the street once in a while. I'd play in the yard and come in and out the way kids do. The funny thing was, you could have the mother looking out her window onto the front yard and the daughter looking out her front window onto the yard and you'd never have known there was a division between them.

I don't ever remember her doing anything crazy. It was more like having that sense of her and her being in a cage was the proof. Otherwise she sat there quietly, joining in the conversation when someone spoke to her. She dressed in cotton house dresses and wore her hair pinned in a roll. She was heavy-bodied, in her late twenties or maybe early thirties.

Her mother had taken care of her like that for about fifteen years so she must have gone out of her head when she was an adolescent.

I remember seeing that she had a white chamber pot tucked by the bed. The mother had to do everything for her, cook her meals and hand them through to her, take the dishes and wash them, empty the chamberpot. The girl kept her part of the room straight and made her own bed.

The mother said she was violent when she got bad.

It must not have been one of those hot places now that I think of it. It must have been a place with a winter because the mother had a fur coat and in one of her daughter's violent spells the fur coat saved her life.

She told my mother that once when her girl had gone through a long sensible period with the two of them sitting and sewing she had suddenly remembered that she had to go to the store before it closed. When the girl saw her mother putting her fur coat on she knew she would be put back in her cage and she grabbed up the sewing scissors and attacked her.

The mother said only her fur coat saved her but it was almost ruined. She had to take it to be resewn.

... five hundred dollars ...

'... five hundred dollars, which at that time was a lot of money. They made a down payment on a farm, got them a little house built and got their farming equipment. Beezer was the type of man that could make money on a rock pile. So she never wanted for anything while she was living with Beezer except she nagged him for so many years he finally went to chasing another woman, and she'll *still* drag that up and talk about it and just get herself all worked up.

'I told her Hell! that's water under the dam. Why don't you forget it.

'She was seventeen when they got married and he was twenty-eight. He was eleven years older'n she was.'

'I remember when I was a kid Aunt Ethel always snubbed me and I used to get my feelings hurt,' I said. 'I never could understand what it was about me that made me so inferior in her eyes.'

'Honey, she did everybody. Boy, but I tell you I really laid her in the shade out there in that little place ... out there on Byers that Wayne and his daddy built for us.

'You know that night you and Velma went out with those boys and the boys just got a bunch of beer and went to drinking it and the other girls went to drinking it and you and Velma just come home? You remember Ethel was going to let Velma stay for two weeks and when you girls come home Velma told Ethel all that story. Well, *you* had explained it when you come home why you was home so early. And Ethel told me the next day, Well, I don't know whether ... I just don't think I'll *leave* Velma over here for two weeks ... the kind of *friends* Jessie's got ... Boy I let her have it! Man, I mean I fairly let her have it! I said, Jessie's got *just* as nice friends or probably *nicer* ones than Velma's got so don't you throw off on Jessie! And I said, I'm going to tell you another damned thing ... She'd been whining over how when Velma was going to school that the kids wouldn't have nothing to do with her. I said, You dress her up in silks and satins and velvets and half of those little kids down there have to wear cotton and rags. And you made a damned snob out of her. And she's so hateful nobody can't stand her. And I said, That's the reason she can't have friends. And I said, You betcha! I'd be most happy for you to take her home. I don't wantchou to leave her!'

'Poor Velma.'

'Well, you know the effect Ethel has on you!

'One day she got me to the point where I was just ready to cut her throat and I told her a few things. She turned around and went in the kitchen and went to washing dishes and humming a tune. Directly she come back in there and I was still just seething and she said (my mother's voice goes prissy and whiny), I shouldn'ta answered you back awhile ago then you wouldn'ta talked to me like that. She said The Bible says *a soft answer turneth away wrath.* Brother! I tell you the *truth* I'm surprised my hair didn't catch on fire!

'Another thing, she made me mad over there in Albuquerque. She kept digging me about my church. I said, Ethel, why don't you get the Bible out and read in there what it says about people with a forked tongue. I said, You might just learn something!

'And I told her there in Texas one time, I said, If the day ever comes, Ethel, when you realize that *you alone* will never be able to change the whole world! I said, Even Jesus Christ couldn't do that ... I said, When you learn that you alone *cannot* change the whole world and that you're not right and the whole world wrong, then you're going to be a happier person! Because, I said, *Nobody's* going to conform and live the way *you* want them to just because *you* want them to!'

'That piece of information must have been hard on her.'

'Well, I think the Lord will be very good to Ethel because she has been so desperate about her trying. She has wanted so much to be a Christian. But Jessie, my idea of Christianity gives this to you. It gives you contentment. Now the year and a half or two years that I lived a good Mormon life, give up my cigarettes ... didn't drink coffee ... Honey, my health was perfect! I didn't have to go to the doctor. I didn't have all these stumbling blocks in front of me. Well, the Bible *tells* you that you won't have them! And I didn't....'

'Yeah, but when you do get the stumbling blocks the Bible tells you how you're supposed to bear with your burdens.'

'Right ...' (a musing voice) 'I don't mean that everything's going to be made perfect for you. But you *should* have *peace* in your own inner self. You should have some *peace*....'

'Yeah.'

'And I don't believe Ethel's ever had a peaceful moment in her life. She was born in misery and she's going to die in misery. And I've got a lot of that in me, but thank God not as much.'

(no change of tone she goes right into ...)

'I could go around him but I can't see ten feet.'

(a big slow truck in front of us)

'Maybe you better not!' I said, laughing.

'I mean ... the way the road is.'

'Well, that's what I had in mind too, Mama.'

'Get Mama out another cigarette. We'll have to get around him if we're ever going to get anywhere, that's for damned sure! I can't tell whether that car's coming or going but I believe it's coming. Thank you, hon.'

Beezer was small ...

Beezer was small and wiry, maybe five seven and maybe a hundred twenty-five pounds. He was in his early thirties when he married Ethel. She was seventeen and a classic beauty, curvaceous but slim with dark hair and black eyes and a heart-shaped face. He caught her at just the right moment between her girlhood when she was so skinny that she wore her high shoes out by knocking her ankle bones together when she walked, and her womanhood when she moved to two hundred pounds and stayed there. Her sisters married when they were fifteen and her brother's wife was fourteen but Ethel had hung a little longer on the vine as a part of her total character which was quietly religious. She came to be a powerful woman manifesting God as her own condition but that was later.

At seventeen she was timorous and even frightened. She ripped a piece of her dress off scrambling panicked through a barbed wire fence running away from the first car she ever saw coming toward her down the road.

She was my mother's oldest sister and my mother told me she wouldn't have had Beezer even then, despite his being a good match, if she hadn't overheard her step-brother Lonny planning with some friends of his to rape her.

Lonny was a shiftless lunk the old man brought with him from his first marriage. He still wet the bed when he was a grown-up man. My mother always contended he was half-witted from the old man beating him in the head. Besides which she'd say, 'He couldn't ever think of anything worthwhile. He had his daddy to live up to.'

So Ethel, who in a different time and place could have been a meditative virgin all her life, cut her losses and relocated her spirit in power and her person in pride by marrying Beezer.

They were the well-off relatives all the time I was growing up. Beezer owned the land he farmed cotton on and he made good crops year after year. He was a hard-working, hard-living man. His size never stopped him. He kept a woman in town for thirty years, the same woman. When she died he didn't get another one.

Everybody knew about it but I can't imagine anyone ever mentioned it to him, except maybe Ethel, but she didn't have much say over him. She couldn't even prevail upon him to keep beer out of the icebox. Every Thanksgiving we used to congregate at their place and as the women started laying out the cooked meats and baked cakes and pies there would always be a point when the icebox got opened and there would be some beer. Ethel was mortified and shamed to the heart by that blatant instance of sin.

It was sin with a certain amount of work back of it. To keep in beer Beezer had to cross three counties to get to where it was Wet. Most of Texas voted Dry, most people agreeing with my Aunt Ethel.

Dancing and playing cards are also on the devil's list of tools to hook souls with, as are 'by-words'. I could never say 'gosh' or 'gee' or 'darn' around my Aunt Ethel without turning up in her evening prayers.

Fundamentalism is an up and down philosophy. Think of Billy Sol Estes, another Texan, who used some of the thousands of dollars he bilked his friends and neighbours out of, before they caught him, to build a swimming pool where unmarried boys and girls weren't allowed to swim at the same time. His business philosophy was 'Get into a man deep enough and you've got a partner.'

Beezer's woman in town and his beer were the cross Ethel had to bear. That and his driving. He drove everywhere he went as close to a hundred miles an hour as he could get. That's not uncommon on the plains with the roads laid out so flat and straight.

Beezer wore out a car a year, but not by just the driving. It was his pleasure to chase jackrabbits. He kept a shotgun over the back seat and whenever a jackrabbit crossed the road in front of him he'd just turn the car into the field after it yelling to whoever was in the back, 'Hand me that shotgun!'

Ethel held nightly prayers before bedtime and when we'd visit it always meant we'd gather in her bedroom, standing in a circle around her with our eyes lowered while she was on her knees in the middle. She used those sessions to get back at anybody who had irritated her during the day.

'Dear Lord,' she'd intone, 'help Mae to shield her tongue. She doesn't know how much harm she does and how many she hurts.' And I would give a quick glance under my eyelids toward my mother who would be standing with her fists clenched, biting her sharp tongue to keep from interfering with Aunt Ethel's heavenly conversation.

Beezer was never at those prayer meetings. He always came back from town late. But he was always up early the next day and out in the field.

He died a few years ago and Ethel sold the farm for a hundred and fifty thousand dollars and built a yellow brick house in town. Velma, her daughter, told me that she's loosened up to the point of wearing a little pale lipstick when she goes out to shop.

Getting off the farm is a powerful influence even on a woman in her sixties.

When my cousin Velma ...

When my cousin Velma was a kid she was skinny and knobby with cottony fly-away hair and a built-in twist to her mouth. That twist always suited what she had to say. She always aggravated me. She grew up to be a thoroughly pleasant woman but all the time she was a kid she was a whiner and a grabber. If we went looking for rocks when the time came to show them, my best rocks would somehow have got into her pile. If we were going out to do something fun just when I started liking it Velma would start whining to go home andd we'd go home.

Her mother, Ethel, always gave in to her. She was convinced that Velma was delicate. Really I think she enjoyed having her puny kid being as bossy as she was.

I did have a good two weeks visiting Velma once when she was about twelve and I was about fourteen. She had entered a radio disk jockey contest to meet Eddie Arnold, a famous figure in country music in those days. Every penny she could beg and steal went for postcards to write votes for herself in to the station.

Every afternoon at two we were at the radio to hear. 'Well now! Velma Leary is still ahead!'

Or even better to hear, 'Well now! Our leader yesterday was Pearl Holiday but we've just received one hundred and eighty-three cards for Velma Leary! That puts Velma back in the lead by one hundred and twenty. Good going, Velma! Keep those cards coming in!'

The two of us got writer's cramp filling out cards. We were certain the station was ethical so we were hung up on disguising our handwriting and changing the phrases around but keeping them short. 'My vote's for Velma Leary.' 'Here's another vote for Velma Leary.' 'I'm for Velma Leary.'

A lot of girls entered the contest but it finally boiled down to three or four who were serious enough to sit all day long writing out votes for themselves.

Anyway, Velma won. And I enjoyed it as much as she did. She was introduced to Eddie Arnold on the radio program and they exchanged two or three sentences and he gave her a copy of his latest record.

The next summer when we visited she had been gloriously saved. She had broken all her cowboy records except the religious ones and she threw away her lipstick, all of which thrilled her mother to death. But I was really bored. All we did was visit a fat country girl friend of hers who had been gloriously saved by the same revivalist. The whole conversation was about how great it was to be gloriously saved and how great it was going to be to go to heaven.

But much earlier than that, when we were kids instead of sensible adolescents, I used to hate her a lot of the time.

One year Ethel wrote that they were coming for a visit and my mother said, 'Please don't get in a fight with Velma. I've had a fight with Ethel the last three times I saw her and this time I mean to have a visit that doesn't end in a fight but if you two kids get started we won't be able to keep out of it.' She knew how hard it was to get along with Velma most of the time but she asked me to grit my teeth and bear it.

And I did. I gritted my teeth when she took my best rocks. I gritted my teeth when she whined. I gritted my teeth when she tromped around in a little piece of garden I had planted, humming to herself and looking up at the sky like she didn't know what she was doing.

It was a miracle to all of us but we got through the whole visit without a fight. It helped my Aunt Ethel's disposition to be given her way in everything. She got almost sweet. But Velma had just got worse and worse.

The time came for them to leave. Aunt Ethel was putting on her hat. My mother said, 'Velma's already in the car, honey. Why don't you go out and say goodbye.'

So I went out and climbed into the back seat alongside Velma. As I looked at her all the things she'd done for the past two weeks came rolling up in my mind and I punched her in the nose.

75

She screamed of course and continued screaming despite my shocked stammering apologies, and the two women came rushing out.

'She *hit* me and I wasn't doing anything to her! She just climbed right into the car and hit me!'

Ethel and my mother were at it then, telling each other off at the top of their lungs, with Ethel clutching Velma and Velma trying desperately to encourage a nose bleed without luck, wailing all the time like a stuck pig.

We stood in the yard and watched the car disappear down the road, dust and gravel blowing up into a cloud back of it.

From Abilene to Lubbock ...

From Abilene to Lubbock, Snyder, Post: we cleared Caprock and hit the pure flat plains. I can't describe the ease and relief I feel when I see all the way to the clear horizon, all around.

One evening when Velma and I were kids and were playing in the half dark of the front porch it started to look as if there was some big fire in the far distance. The sky glowed red and the glow became larger until it took up half the sky in that direction. And in the wake of the colour rose an enormous full orange moon. Texas full moons have the gift of being seen the instant they surface.

Stand in a perfect half circle. The far line of the horizon is exactly horizontal. That line extends as far as you can see, left or right. Below that line is one colour, above it is another colour. You are standing on the exact line of it. Your feet are on earth and your head is in the air. Roughly speaking you are a 90° vertical line. You are a definite addition to the landscape, that is you *are* holding down that piece of ground and you're human.

That moon rose right up and the colour with it. It became smaller as it rose, becoming finally pure white and brilliant.

And still that horizontal holds. The light from the sky illuminates the flat plain.

I just don't hardly ...

'I just don't hardly cook at all anymore. I'm just getting terrible,' Ethel broke up laughing at this image of herself.

Her house in town was made of brick, the floors shone, and the fixtures in the two bathrooms. The bedrooms were fully decorated, walls filled with framed photographs of her children and grandchildren. In the bathroom little metal filigree stands held guest soap, round yellow lemons. And there were paintings on the wall that she had made herself. There was no doubt that her lifestyle had changed. There was no cotton bib apron on a hook in the kitchen.

We were in a small restaurant located two blocks down the street.

'Well, this looks like a real nice place to eat,' Mae looked around. Formica top tables and chrome chairs with padded backs and seats. The place held mostly middle-aged women and one table of young men, one still had on his straw hat, leaning back against the wall with his chair tilted onto its hind legs.

The waitress was about forty-five and wore glasses with flowers and small rhinestones in a slight upward sweep at the outside corners. She wasn't wearing a wig but her hair was intricately dressed, as good as a

French court lady could have done, if she used her own hair.

She stood at the table, her pencil and pad were out and ready.

'Hello, Miz Leary. Yawl ready to order?'

'We haven't made our minds up yet, Eunice.'

Eunice pocketed her pad and pencil and smiled, walked away.

We examined the menu. The menus had a border of cattle brands around the outside edge.

'They always have fried chicken here on Wednesdays,' Ethel said.

'I wish she hadn't hurried away. I wanted to ask her if they make their chicken salad fresh here. Do you know? Do they make their own chicken salad?'

'Well, we can surely ask.'

Eunice returned.

'Is your chicken salad really fresh? Did you make it today? I've just had a longing this whole trip for some good fresh chicken salad.'

'No ma'am, it's not fresh. I mean, nobody made any this morning.'

'Jessie, what are *you* having?'

'I want the Mexican Plate and iced tea.'

Eunice wrote it down.

'They make good chili here, too,' Ethel said.

'I'd love some good chili. I feel like ordering that Mexican Plate myself. But I wouldn't be able to sleep tonight. What kind of chili do you put on your Mexican Plate?'

'We usually put red but if you like green better he can put green.'

'Oh my, I'd like that. But it would just tear up my stomach. I'd be sick for a week.'

'Well, Mama, why don't you get something that won't tear up your stomach.'

'What are you having, Ethel?'

'I'm going to have a chicken-fried steak.'

'I guess I will, too.'

'You both want those cooked well done?'

'Heavenly days, yes! I can't stand pink meat.'

Eunice left.

'And they make the *best* breakfasts! I come here two or three times a week for breakfast. There are a few women friends of mine that we meet here and have breakfast together. This place is close enough so I can walk.'

'What's the matter with that brand new Buick you've got, Ethel?

Dontchew ever get that new Buick out of the garage for anything but to wash it?'

'They recognize me, you know. Everybody knows everybody here. They all know I don't have a license.

'Of course I *use* it. If I want to go to Lubbock or over to Frank's I just get in the car and go. Sometimes they stop me and sometimes they don't. There's one boy, cutest thing in his uniform you ever saw, he'll see me and he'll just grin and wave me on by.'

'Ethel, you *must* drive well enough to be able to get a license. You've been driving for years!'

'I was in there about ten days ago getting tested. We drove around with that silly examiner just saying turn right, now turn left. You know how they do. I do just fine when I'm by myself but those old examiners always make me nervous. Well, when we got back to the license place I said, Do I get my license? And he said, Lady, you're lucky to be alive!' She started laughing again.

Marvin answered the door ...

Marvin answered the door in the bottom half of a set of pale blue pajamas.

'We tried to call you,' Ethel said. 'There's something wrong with the phone number you gave me.'

'Well Jessie! We knew you were due here but we thought you'd changed your mind. We expected you about a month ago.'

I gave him a hug and my hands slid around on his bare back.

'Aw, Velma's in the bathroom putting on lotion and she slathered some of it on me.'

'I'll go get her out of the bathroom.' I headed back through the house.

'Velma?'

'Who *is* that?' her voice came, irritable and suspicious.

'Come on. Get out of there. You can't stay in the bathroom all your life!'

'Who *is* that?'

'Jessie.'

'Jessie *who*?'

'Your cousin, Jessie! How many Jessies you got around this place?'

The door flew open. Velma was in a pale pink Babydoll nightgown. She was working on her face, so she wore a pink lace cap that covered all of her hair.

'Oh Jessie.' We hugged and she started crying.

'Who'd you come with? Is Aunt Mae here?'

'She's in the front room with Aunt Ethel.'

'Oh Lord, is Mama here? I better get dressed. Well I'll do it in a while.'

Barefoot and babydolled, with cream all over her face she started toward the front room, sauntering. She reached out and grabbed a towel as we passed through the kitchen and she entered the livingroom wiping the cream from her face onto the towel.

'Oh Velma!' her mother wailed. 'You'll *ruin* that towel honey!'

'I hafta wipe my face on something if I'm gonna kiss Aunt Mae.'

She tossed the towel onto a chair. Ethel snatched it up and looked underneath to see whether the grease had got onto the fabric.

I've been a practising lawyer ...

'I've been a practising lawyer now for three years. I've got an office set up in Root.'

'He's just turned into everybody that can't pay's *poor* lawyer,' Velma complained. 'He's so tender-hearted he gets all the people that can't pay nothing! And they hang around all the time. I don't get to see him more than a couple of hours in any twenty-four.'

She was sprawled sideways across a chair with her legs hiked and one foot circled back around to let her paint the toenails dark red.

'He got the *highest* score in the whole state when he took his bar exam,' she said. 'Him and a woman tied for first place!'

'How did you manage to get a law degree?' I asked. 'I thought you had to stay home after your daddy had his stroke.'

'Well, I couldn't go to Austin. But they put a law school in in Lubbock. So I could live here and see to the farm and go to classes, too.'

'I just lived for when he got his degree and passed his exam,' Velma started on the other foot. 'I thought I'd get to see him then, but no. They telephone him day and night and if they don't get him at his office they telephone him here. Or show up. One woman was here almost five hours a few days ago, just bawling.'

'Velma, I'm not away that much of the time. Velma likes to have me at home. That was Mrs Gutierrez. Her husband ran away with a twelve-year-old girl. The girl's parents put papers out on him. The problem was keeping the federal government out of it. He took her to New Mexico.'

'What did his wife want? Did she want to divorce him?'

'Naw. He'd been caught and sent back. The kid was back with her folks. The wife wanted him to get out of jail. She got the girl's parents to drop charges. So now they're all back over there working for Mr Holiday. It seems like everything's O.K.'

We sat up talking, the three of us, until three in the morning. Mae and Ethel had gone back over to Ethel's house.

When I was ready for bed and said goodnight Velma said, 'I'm going to stay up half the night. I've just been doing that lately. So I tend to sleep late. When you wake up in the morning wake me up and we'll go over and see Frank. But you're going to have to wake me up. Otherwise I'll sleep until well into the afternoon.'

The next morning I found the coffee and made some, read through the morning paper and woke Velma up at about eleven.

She had come by a minute toy poodle. It bounced like elastic in the bedroom when I opened the door. There was an elegant arrangement of furniture that let the tiny animal scamper up the side of the bed to where it slept, on a cushion on the pillows at the head of the bed. The poodle slept with its head between the husband and wife.

The night before while we talked, Velma and Marvin had stood the creature on a newspaper and trimmed the fur on its legs with fingernail scissors.

While Velma turned one way and then the other to make sure it was daylight on both sides, the dog ran up and down the 'arrangement' with little leaps.

'Good Lord! It feels like daybreak!'

To drive ten miles to see her brother, Velma creamed her face and cleaned it off, pulled her hair back severely so that she looked skinned and stared at herself critically, drew her eyebrows on with a black pencil, (if that's provincialism so's Elizabeth Taylor) used the kind of mascara that makes eyelashes 'grow' until they're as good as artificial ones, put blue eyeshadow on so that all the skin between her eyelids and her eyebrows was covered, put on face make-up including rouge and lipstick. End of phase one.

Then she put on a champagne coloured wig with a bouffant styling that made her stand a good foot taller. She intended to be informal and this particular wig had a little neck knot of curls back of and below the enormous helmet effect; the cluster of curls was held by a black velvet clip-on bow.

Then she went back to the closet in her bedroom, the poodle skipping alongside. She put on a new peach coloured silk shirt, a pair of Levi's, hand-tooled boots, and a denim jacket.

We drove over to Frank's in Velma's Oldsmobile; the poodle went with us.

'Frank and Jimmie-Sue haven't seen my new dog,' Velma tooled the car around efficiently. 'She was *supposed* to be pure apricot. Apricot's really rare. That's why we paid so much for her. See. You can see the apricot here and here. She was supposed to be apricot all over.'

The tiny dog watched us as intently as if she watched a tennis match, her quick beads of eyes flicked back and forth and back.

Frank bought ...

'Frank bought sixteen pairs of pants today!' Jimmie-Sue said.

'Sixteen?'

'She was supposed to be pure apricot but she wasn't. But we couldn't take her back by that time.' Velma was holding the tiny furry face pressed against hers. She put the dog onto the floor and it circled the room, each tiny foot going down like a pin-prick.

'How'd you come to buy sixteen pairs of pants,' I asked. 'You turning into the last of the big-time spenders?'

'We went into town so he could get a new pair of khakis....' Jimmie-Sue started to tell the story.

Frank picked it up. 'They're not going to make a hundred percent cotton khaki pants anymore.'

'Alice was waiting on us,' Jimmie-Sue said. 'She said Well, those'll be the last one hundred percent cotton khakis you'll ever get.'

'I hate to work in that blended stuff, that polyester. It's no improvement. It gets too hot and sticks to you.'

I remember once going swimming with Frank and Velma. Or what I call swimming. I never learned to do more than float. I mean I can't turn my head and breathe as I go, so what I do is I get my arms and legs going with my face in the water and every so often I roll over, totally, and breathe; then I roll over again and go some more. But that doesn't mean I don't enjoy it.

Particularly when it's so hot that even the rocks wilt. That day was that hot. The three of us were in a pickup and going across flat shimmering land. I couldn't imagine where we were going. The truck wheeled right, onto a dirt road and we stopped. No river, no lake, nothing in sight. We walked off the dirt road a hundred yards or so and there was a hole in the ground like a giant well. It measured about thirty feet across. We started climbing down the path, past a small cottonwood. The bottom was a circle of pure blue water, it was so clear you could see rock ledges ten feet below, around the edges. The middle just went on down to black.

'They've never found a bottom to this.'

Looking up, the dirt sides were dotted with mud swallow nests and the birds were home. There was a constant chittering from them and at intervals they would cut loose together and fly in a lovely spiral around and around at the top.

We were down about sixty feet. Going down it was like each step moved into a cooler ridge of air. Up above, where the swallows flew and did their quick banking to avoid the walls, the heat shimmered and shook at the lip of the well. It was a magic place.

'So Frank just bought every pair of khakis they had in his size and then we went down the street to *Albertson's,* and he bought every pair of khakis *they* had!' Jimmie-Sue finished with a flourish.

It was a good story. Frank, handsome as ever, that Indian look really paid off, leaned back in his leather recliner and grinned.

'So your plan is to never get fat and never get skinny and never buy another pair of pants,' I said.

'That's about it.'

When I had to go out to the car for my purse I saw that Velma's dog had deposited a neat pile in the middle of the floor in the next room.

'You better go in the next room and clean up after your dog before Jimmie-Sue sees it,' I told Velma in a whisper when I came back.

'The salesman kept bringing them out and bringing them out. Finally she said Well I think I want a Buick that's just like the one Mae's got. So Frank called around and got one just like Aunt Mae's and that's the one she's got now,' Jimmie-Sue was saying.

'What does she do that's so wrong?'

'She just drives like she's still on a country road,' Frank grinned. 'She moves into the flat middle and goes and nothing can't stop her till she gets to where she's going.'

'Well, she's just a menace!' Jimmie-Sue said.

Aunt Ethel decided to cook a dinner for this visit, so we all, Velma and I, Marvin, Frank and Jimmie-Sue, converged on her house, ate, and then Mama and I got our bags into the Buick and kissed and hugged all around and drove off.

A letter from Ethel to Mae says, 'Velma just broke down bawling. She kept saying, That's the last time I'll ever see Jessie alive.'

84

Everything begins as a dot ...

Everything begins as a dot at the level of the horizon. The dot gets bigger as it comes closer ... reaches full size and stops ... a farm, a stand of mesquite trees, a humpbacked metal cotton gin with wagons standing derelict around the yard, their insides fuzzy with bits and tufts of cotton.

Or ... a combination gas station grocery store with two or three men in khakis or bib overalls and summer straw hats, hunkered back on their heels talking in the shade of the wall.

They glance up briefly when the Model-A Ford drives in.

'There's some monkies in that cage out back. Why dontcha take your little girl back for a look.'

That cage stood on hard-packed dirt with no trees. A couple of burlap toe-sacks had been laid onto one corner of the top with rocks to hold them down, for a shade.

I broke some cookies into pieces and threw the pieces toward the cage for the monkies to grab and fuss over. Mama stood watching, pleased as she always was when a treat came along. One bit of cookie bounced off a bar and back onto the ground just out of reach of the small crabby hand at the end of a hairy stick of arm.

I went forward to pick it up, leaning over.

The next thing I knew, I had been got. That hand grabbed my hair and pulled me closer and then the others got in on the game. Cookies forgotten they were all, or as many as there was room for, hands and feet together, in my hair, pulling. I was screaming.

My father came running with a stick he picked up as he came. The station owner came running. They got me loose.

When I was little ...

When I was little the cousin I dearly loved was Billy-Bob. He was my mother's brother's boy and a few months younger than me. He had a sweet nature, really soft and open and, now thinking back, innocent.

My mother was really close to her brother, my Uncle Peter, and even to his wife Maxine, despite the way Maxine had of going to bed during her monthly periods, which made my mother purse her mouth in disgust. My mother figured a fine distinction between womanly weakness and self-indulgence; being really on her brother's side when it really came down to it.

So Billy-Bob and I saw a lot of each other and I took his side in the same way, and carried it a lot farther along than he would have done, him being gentle. When his little brother Curtis was born sickly so Billy-Bob was doubly deprived I hated the new baby for him.

When Curtis could walk and became the classic tag-along I got rid of him at least once by walking around inside the chicken house with the door locked saying loudly, 'Look at the little baby kittens. Look at the puppies!'

'There ain't no puppies or kittens in there!' Curtis yelled through the wall.

'Look at the baby giraffes and the baby elephants!'

'There ain't no baby elephants in there!'

•And when he was so teased by it that he was pounding on the door I walked out, cool, and he rushed in, triumphant.

'See! See! There ain't no....'

And I closed the door back of him and latched it and Billy-Bob and I headed for the watermelon field.

The bottom fell out of melons that year and made them not worth the picking. We would walk along the rows busting ripe melons and eating only the heart. It was a luxury that took some heroism; the sand was hot as a frying pan and we were bare-footed. We had to hit our feet against the soft dirt with each step hard enough to dislodge the top surface and get into the slightly cooler under part.

We weren't supposed to go into the watermelons at all because what if a miracle happened and one day the prices were up, then that field would be a crop. But that never happened and we went almost daily into the ripening then rotting melons as part of our rounds.

And we played mumblety-peg outside the kitchen door with a pocket knife. And we swung in an old tire hung from a chinaberry tree.

It wasn't until supper time when we were sitting down and Aunt Maxine said, 'Where's Curtis?' that we remembered. I went out and unlatched the shed.

It must have been a hellish day for a little kid, all day long in the hot chicken house. But even now my inclination is that he deserved it.

Until I was ten Billy-Bob and I were 'favourite cousins.' Then we moved for good to New Mexico and started living with my Aunt Hannah and I came to be favourite cousins with my cousin Bud. Bud would let me choose whether I wanted to wash or dry the dishes in exchange for telling a story while we worked.

One of the running stories was: 'What if tomorrow morning we went to the flume and we found the biggest fish in the world.'

The flume only measured ten feet across but that didn't interfere with the projection. It was a slightly wider place in a nearby irrigation ditch where a wooden trough covered with slick green moss brought water down from a ditch at a higher level. We could go to the top of the incline and get shooshed along the trough and dumped head over heels into the ditch.

'Well, we'd put it in a tank on a flatcar and we could go all over the country charging dimes to see the biggest fish in the world.'

The final image included a lot more. We finally had in mind something like a traveling medicine show, a kind of village of entertainers all living and travelling on adjacent flatcars. We ironed out all the wrinkles like what kind of tent would keep passersby from seeing the fish until we let them. We got the whole theory straight but we never found the fish. It wasn't even a disappointment. The fish was the least of it.

But it was years later when I was a grownup woman with my first child two years old that I made a trip to Texas to my Uncle Peter's. Billy-Bob was over six feet tall and weighed nearly two hundred pounds. We couldn't look each other in the eye. It was truly awkward as if blood and time froze up.

'Well! Ain't you two gonna give each other a kiss?' and we got through a routine of cheek-pecking.

After supper when everybody else was talking we walked out back of the house.

It's hard to explain what the plains look like if you've never been there. The land is totally flat on all sides all the way to the horizon. There's a lot of space and the sky is huge. There was a sunset. Billy-Bob said, faltering and gentle, 'I guess it's hard to stay favourite cousins when you move away and when you're playing every day with somebody else.' To let me off the hook. As if we're any of us off that hook. Our natural infidelities.

But it breaks my heart to think how he tried to tell me he understood what had happened and didn't hold it against me.

When Billy-Bob married ...

When Billy-Bob married he married a girl whose daddy was a sharecropper. They were rock bottom poor and, according to Billy-Bob's mother, a little backward. My Aunt Maxine wouldn't have been satisfied with anybody Billy married and that poor girl had a lot to put up with from her and from Billy's little sister who took the same tone.

When Alvina would come over with Billy for a visit they'd do things like ask her if her breakfast dishes were washed.

Alvina seemed alright to me the couple of times I met her. She was thin and pale with dark hair. Maxine asked Billy once why he couldn't have found somebody a little more healthy.

This is a story about a kind of sorrow and I should really have started it a different way, with some sense of how close country people felt to the radio in the thirties and forties, before television.

Aunt Maxine used to talk as off-handed about Roy and Hank and Gene as if they lived down the road. That was Roy Acuff and Hank Williams and Gene Autry. If you came on it late and think you've got taste in country music you'll probably smirk at the idea of Gene Autry, but at that time he was ranked right in there with the others.

The place Alvina's daddy worked had an old wood-frame house that the family lived in. It was two stories high and had a permanent lean away from the direction the sandstorms crossed the plains there. It was really run down, like it could go in the next wind that hit it.

Inside, the house had more rooms than the family had furniture for. They had a table and chairs in the room alongside the kitchen, and everybody had old iron bedsteads fitted out with feather mattresses but that was mostly it. You could go into a lanky old room that wouldn't have anything in it but a rocking chair next to a high bare window that looked out onto nothing but the horizon. And there were rooms that didn't have anything in them at all.

One of the things they did have was a table-model radio.

When Hank Williams died Alvina's daddy took the radio out to the woodpile and smashed it up with his axe as a gesture of grief.

He said that with Hank dead there wouldn't be any more music worth listening to.

Didn't Billy have ...

'Didn't Billy have a stroke or something?'

'He works for this cotton mill, honey, and that lint got into the bottom part of his lungs and just packed. Of course, you don't use the bottom parts of your lungs very much so you can survive with that easy enough. But what he should of done is sued that mill for an income for the rest of his life, then got disability and social security! He could of got it for him and his wife and all those kids!'

'How many kids does he have?'

'Five. They had twins you know after they had those three. Little twin girls.'

'How are they? What are the kids like?'

'That's the *same* damned truck I was behind a hundred miles back! I let him go around me!'

'Mama, you're only going fifty miles an hour.'

'Well, their oldest boy's about seventeen or eighteen now. Or sixteen. And he's real smart. Their oldest girl, Hazel, they browbeat her until she rebelled and left home. She just lately started working at the hospital. The little middle one, the little blonde girl, she's a sweet little girl (shift to mournful) but she's growing up too. I don't know ... the little twins are about six or seven.'

'Billy-Bob and his wife get along alright now?'

'They'd have always got along alright if it hadn't been for Maxine. Maxine and Pearl was sneaking around and watching her and accusing her of running around with other men when Billy was truck driving. Telling Billy I don't know what. All that stuff ... till she probably did start running around. But I wouldn't of blamed her!'

'I better quit talking. My throat's starting to hurt.'

By the time I was fifteen ...

By the time I was fifteen I had read enough books to be a common kind of victim. I believed that there was a world I hadn't got to yet that focused on intelligence and wit and graces that were attainable. By the time I was sixteen I had all the grandiose reasoning that let me 'choose' in my mind to be an artist. I had rejected being a millionaire as only one of my options and without a look back. My reasoning was that the right kind of millionaires pay court to artists.

You can see how far afield the books had led me.

There was no justification for believing that any of those choices was more than the fantasy it certainly was.

To walk forward in the classroom at school and sharpen a pencil was an exercise in will and drama. I would invent a story to let me cross the floor.

I had already gone through a bout when I was thirteen with chorea. At its easiest it was a twitch in my fingers or a slight jerk in my elbow. At its worst, as my mother put it, Jessie can be walking along a perfectly smooth piece of sidewalk and fall flat on her face!

I was a sore subject. My hemlines were uneven, my socks always worked down into my shoes and my spirit only felt comfortable when it was miles back in me.

I talked too much or too little, too shy to deserve attention or exact to the point of being pedantic, in desperation. I was afraid most of the time.

All of this describes a classic case.

Something was bound to happen internally. The need was finally bound to be past bearing.

My Aunt Maxine hoarded sugar during the Second World War. It was sugar she came by legally. The government gave extra rations to farmers for canning. But she didn't use it all. And, given the shortage, she didn't want to return it. What if next year there wasn't any? So she 'canned' the sugar in glass mason jars. She made a syrup of sugar and water and put it on the shelves in the cellar alongside the peaches and plums and green beans.

That sugar-water turned into the loveliest sight to see. The sugar formed crystals inside the jars. When you'd bring one of those jars of sugar out into the sunlight it could practically throw rainbows.

Aunt Maxine was bothered by the manifest sugar. She was afraid that government inspectors might recognize what was going on. But they never came around. The war did end and the sugar did finally get used up. But while it was being stored....

I feel like I was like that. Something caught in abeyance with a lot of transformation going on and a heartfelt fear of discovery. It felt illegal.

Aunt Ada came ...

Aunt Ada came from Texas on the Greyhound bus, to visit with Mae. The three of us sat in the small living room watching Zoorama on the television. The two sisters raised their voices to be heard above the sound. Sometimes they would look at each other or at me.

Aunt Ada's voice was wind across miles of plain, a vacuum pulled high into her nose.

'I felt like it was the other mother's turn. I was there for two months and I told Marydel and Duke, It's *her* turn. I'll just go and visit with Mae for awhile. Duke's mother said, Now, are you sure you've got somewhere to go? Just like sugar. Well, you know Marydel! She never would hear a word against *me*! She piped right up and said, Mama has plenty of places to go! Plenty of people want Mama to come and visit! She said, You don't have to go anywhere if you don't want to, Mama, you can stay right here! But I said, No, it's her turn and I want to go visit with Mae awhile.'

Aunt Ada's face, all those dry-weather lines, broke into pieces when she smiled.

On Zoorama they were feeding the crocodiles.

Mae told about a neighbour's little girl, laughing. 'She had her face all twisted up, I'm sure glad I don't have one of those stuck on me. Why doesn't he sit down and stick it between his legs to pee-pee. Why does he just have to stand there and show it?'

Aunt Ada told about Norma-Jean's little girl. When she was three her parents decided she should know how boys were 'made.'

'Did they show her a little baby boy's?' Mae asked.

'No!' Aunt Ada's voice dropped a pitch. 'They showed her Jim's!'

The two women stared at each other.

'They did what?'

'They showed her her *daddy's*!'

Significant looks like pins through the butterfly while the wings still flap.

On Zoorama in Florida the porpoises were trying to talk. There was proof of how, closed into aquariums they were adapting their voices, lowering the pitch, trying to form words.

'What would *you* do,' the scientist makes his point to the interviewer, 'If you found yourself encased in air, held by some obviously intelligent life form, and you wanted to communicate with them?'

Adapt was the gist of that familiar message.

'Isn't that awful! Look at it, Ada! It's just like a little old dried up man! Ooooh! I just couldn't stand to have one of those things near me!'

It was a baby monkey. The head seemed a holder for two enormous eyes, slit for a mouth, wrinkles all over, a little round hairless belly.

'Jessie used to look so pretty when she let me cut her hair and put a permanent in it,' Mae told Ada. They looked at me, their eyes weighing what could have been perfect in me, given a few changes.

It was later that evening that I said, 'I think I'll go with Axel.'

I might still have been stopped if someone had made a joke of it, had let me make a joke of it. The statement sat in the room as black and hard as decision.

'Well, Jessie, if you're sure that's what you want to do.'

Later Mae grieved, 'I think Jessie got married just to leave home.'

Pearl said ...

'Pearl said, That first husband of Jessie's ... where was he from? right in front of a bunch of people ... like they *always* do me ...! I said, He was from Denmark. And she said, And the one she's married to now ... he's a writer? And I said, Yes, he is. She said, She sure did marry a couple of funny guys, didn't she?

'Her husband's a real stupe. He's doing alright but he's working *her* to death because he's getting in the business of trying to make money. He keeps them so far in debt that Pearl's worked til she has stomach ulcers!

'So she says, She sure did marry a couple of funny guys, didn't she? And I said, Well, they may be funny but I'll tell you one damned thing. She got herself a couple of smart ones!

'Boy! She just went to bawling!'

'Oh really!' (laughing)

'Yeah! She just went to bawling. Said, Well, I don't care whether anybody likes ... uh ... what *is* her husband's name ... Edward ...! I guess my folks *don't* like Edward. And they think he's dumb. But *I* don't care ... I said, I didn't even know Edward was in the conversation! I thought we was discussing Jessie's husbands!'

'I don't like to go visiting *anybody* that I feel like I've got to fight for my life or fight to be defending myself all the time!'

I used to love ...

'I used to love to tease that old girl,' Peter said.

'She was so shy,' Maxine said, 'worse than if she'd never married at all.'

When Maxine's brother, Boss, married he found that he had a problem. His wife had a muscle that was grown across the opening to her vagina. After a frustrating period of time he saw to it that she went to a doctor and they learned that the 'problem' was correctable.

'Well, her first husband took her to a doctor too!'

'She had been married before?' I asked.

'For about three days. Then he took her to a doctor and you know what she did? Of course this was years ago and women weren't so simple about ... women didn't just go in and let doctors poke them unless they were sick. So her first husband took her to be examined ... I guess it must have been the first time anything like that ever happened to her ... and she jumped up screaming off the examination table and cut out for home. She told her Mama that LeRoy had taken her to a whorehouse!'

'The second time around it all must have been simpler,' I suggested.

'Oh no!' Maxine was positive. 'She wouldn't have the operation! She just told Boss straight out that she never meant to have an operation.'

'How long did that go on?'

'Oh, for years!'

'I used to love to tease her,' Peter repeated. 'I come in one time, we were all going to have dinner together, and she was setting in a chair all dressed up and as prim and proper. I just walked over and set right down in her lap....'

'Peter just walked right over and set in her lap!' Maxine started laughing.

'She blushed from her feet clear up to the roots of her hair.'

'What finally happened?'

'Aw, she got appendicitis and had to have her appendix out. So Boss made an agreement with the doctor that while she was under he'd just ...'

'He just took care of that other thing, too.'

'And you know,' Maxine said, 'she never did forgive him for that. It's been years and she still holds that against him!'

'Yeah. They've got a couple of kids and *still* she won't turn loose of that grudge she holds about that.'

'How *long* were they married before she got appendicitis,' I asked.

'Oh, for years!'

'That was patient of him to wait around,' I said, 'they were really lucky. She could have gone her whole life long and never got sick with anything strong enough to need an anesthetic for.'

Curtis stuck his foot ...

Curtis stuck his foot up in the air at me.

'You don't *see* that kind of boot where you come from, do you?'

He had a right to be proud. It was a handsome boot.

'Sure I do. If somebody can afford 'em.'

'Naw, I mean, you don't see these boots with pointed toes and heels like that. Those people where you live, they wear ... the kind of boots they wear has square toes and a strap across here.'

'Not all of them,' I said. Then I decided to get him. 'Curtis,' I said, 'There isn't a hippy in the world that doesn't want to be a cowboy.'

His face blushed fiery red. He could just about stand it.

Thirty-thirty's what they ...

'Thirty-thirty's what they usually use?'

'Naw, it was biggern' a thirty-thirty. And it come out right over there. And when it come out....'

'A thirty-ought-six? Is that what they call 'em?'

'Yeah, a thirty-ought-six. It made a hole just about *that* big. And it just come through his hip over here. He said, just like you said, he said he just took and got blood and everything out of there.'

'Aw!'

'You just think what that did to his ... going through his ... *bowels* and *stomach* through there! And ast him ... said ... You wanna go to a doctor?'

'They can patch that up. That's much easier than ... when it goes through your *lungs* is when you get into bad trouble. That would of tore up his kidneys and everything.'

'This time *I'm* talking about ... what I was going to tell you ... see, we don't believe in going to a doctor, you know. So they ast him they said You wanna go to the doctor. He said *No*. He said Get me down that mountain and *baptise* me. Old Brother Gene said they carried him down the mountain and baptised him. Four days later he was out doing his work. Never did go to the doctor.'

'Hmmm.'

'You just *think* about that bullet going plumb through just right there ... plumb through ... and coming out....'

'I'd rather not think about it.'

For their wedding trip ...

For their wedding trip Curtis and Linda drove up through northwest Texas and into Denver. From Denver they dropped south to Albuquerque and stopped at Mae's.

'Curtis's just been eating hamburgers all the way,' Linda half-teased and was half-serious. The tone she used was common to lovers, that teasing tenderness.

'So when we got to Denver we was so tired we thought we'd do something different and instead of stopping in a motel we went to a nice tourist home. It was really comfortable. And we decided that night to have a fancy dinner. Well, the landlady was French and she told us about a French restaurant. So we went there.

'Well, the first thing was we had to wait for a table but the place was real pretty so we decided to go ahead and wait. The next thing was everybody there was dressed up in suits and ties.

'Curtis was just wearing one of his cowboy shirts with the sleeves all rolled up. Of course, we were clean and all.'

'I told Linda They'll just know a Texas boy's been here.'

'We just waited and waited.'

'There was these two old boys that it was clear that was the table we would get. I mean they had finished all their dinner when we first got there. But then they *had* to have some kind of dessert. Then they *had* to have coffee. Lord, you'd have thought they could get through that coffee fast enough. You know those little tiny cups? Well, that's the kind of coffee they had. You'd have thought it was a gallon. And they had a little bit of wine in one of those great big glasses. There wasn't no more than two swallows of coffee in those cups. And there was less wine than that! Well, you should have seen them with those glasses! They *made* over that! They took that little bit of wine and they *rolled* it around, and they *smelled* it. And after all that they'd take one little sip. It must've taken them fifteen minutes to get through that two swallows of coffee and that dinky little bit of wine!'

'We walked right past them. There was another table came free just because of the way they was messing around.'

'The *next* thing was the menu was all in French!'

'You know Curtis! He wasn't about to ask what it said. The waitress came over and....' The two of them started laughing.

'The waitress come over and Curtis ordered a hamburger!'

You heard anybody ...

'You heard anybody say what cotton pulling's going at, Daddy?'
Curtis asked.

'I heard old W.B. say some guy told him he'd pull his at seventy-five
cents. I said You better get him because I said, Most of it's going to be
over a dollar.'

'You know butane's already twenty cents a gallon? They say by the
time we get to pulling it'll be over twenty-five. I tell you something, it's
going to cost to pull a crop like this one.'

'Aw, it won't be so bad. How about diesel? It depends on what
diesel's going at.'

We was setting there ...

'We was setting there,' Aunt Maxine said, 'and my brother had one of
them old watches my daddy bought him with both sides, you know,
you have to push a thing to see ... you know how them used to be.'

'Them old watches that you'd mash the stem and they'd fly open,'
Peter said.

'He *ast* for one of *them* kind of watches,' Maxine continued.

'But *first* he'd had two men come up there and one of them was on
one side of the stage and one of them was on the other side. He give one
of them an *orange* to hold ... says, Now you hold onto this and don't let
it get away! And he give the other one a *box* just about this big a square
and said, Now, you hold that tight where nothing won't get out of
there. And *then* he ast for a watch. And I said, Boss, let him have it! Let
him have yours! Nobody else there had one or wouldn't let him have it.

'So Boss give him his watch. He just looked at it and said This old
watch dudn't look like it's any good, says, I'm just going to shoot it
over yonder across the stage. And he put it in this gun, an old big-

barrelled gun. You could *see* it going across, looked like. Going across there. He looks at Boss and says I'll pay you for that, son, after awhile. Then he went on with his rigamarole, just left Boss setting there. Everybody... all the boys was ateasing him, you know.'

'Lost his watch.'

'Yeah, so directly he got a hat. This old boy that I was with he got his hat and busted four eggs in it and stirred 'em around and around, just stirred and stirred and stirred 'em. Put a lid on and set 'em on ... built a *fire* with some paper. Some of those old candy boxes. You know they always sold candy. And he set that hat on that fire.'

'Was that hat a good 'un?' Curtis interrupted.

'It was a brand-new Stetson!'

'He wouldn't a got *my* hat. Not unless he taken it away from me!'

'Well, Aunt Bea was just having *fits*!

'Then after awhile he said, I guess them eggs is done! and he picked the hat up and pulled that paper off of it ... that hat just *set* up there on that fire. Never burned nor nothing! And he taken that paper off of there and *four chickens* jumped out! Jumped out of that hat!

'Then he fooled around and said, Son, says, have you helt that box good? He said, Yeah. He said, Well, what's in it? Said, I don't know. You give it to me a long time ago. And he was just a *holding* it. This old man ... it was Hank Utely that was holding the box! So he says, Well, he says, Let me see! He says, Open it up. And he opened it up and there was another box in that box, and there was another box in that box. He just kept opening up boxes till he just had a pile of boxes and got down to a little 'un and that *watch* was in it!'

'Uhmmm Uhmmm.'

'Then he said, The *chain's* off of it! Where's the chain! And he says, Son, take a bite of that orange! And he'd give that orange to that guy before he even *got* the watch! And he give this box to this one before he ever even got the watch!'

'Uhmmm Hhmmm.'

'He taken a bite of that orange and when he did he *bit* onto the chain!'

'Well, I'll say!'

'I don't know *how in the world* he done that! Boss just swore that watch never did keep good time after that!'

Well, I'll tell yawl ...

'Well, I'll tell yawl something I don't know whether you ever ... You ever been around Mexkins much?' Curtis asked me.

'She's been around more Mexkins than you have!'

'Well, I don't know. She'd have to be around a whole lot, wouldn't she, Daddy.'

'She's *lived* out there in New Mexico.'

'She lived in Albuquerque for *years* and *years*.'

'Them's a different breed of Mexkins from what we've got out here.'

'Well, they really are.'

'What I was going to tell you, every Mexkin in *this* part of the country will tell you that if you know the right man he can take a dollar bill and lay it on a pile of newspaper and draw one off. Then he just starts cutting them out! That size. And he stacks 'em up *that* high. Do 'em like that and every one'll be a dollar bill!

'They say they can *spend* that money. Old Luke said he had often done that and he bought *everything* with it.

'The guy that told him how to do it said, You won't live *long* though, after you start doing it!

'Old Luke said he bought everything! Said he taken that money and do it like that. And old Ben Sanchez down there, said he seen him do it!

'Ever Mexkin in this country'll tell you they can do that. That *some-body* they know can. Old Ben's daddy told me that his brother got to doing that.'

'How long did he live?'

'He died when he was thirty-six. Then old Ben got hold of it and started doing it.

'What you got to do is worship the devil to be able to do it.'

'Ben?!!'

'Uhmm Hmmm!'

'Ben Sanchez?'

'Yep. And his daddy taken them books, you know he was telling us about that? His daddy found out about his doing that and he taken them books and burnt 'em!'

'You learn how to do it out of a book?' I asked.

'Yeah. You get this book that tells you how.'

'Sounds to me like the guy that's sure to be making the money is the guy that's selling the books!'

'Now this here's the deal though. You can't *buy* the book.'

'Yeah?'

'It's got to be wrote, see, by you ... and then you give it to me ... just like him. His *uncle* give it to him. You don't ever sell it!'

'Oh.'

'Then his uncle whenever he went to die he give it to Ben. It passes on and on.'

'I'd rather be poor and live a long time than be rich and....'

'I'll tell you what ... him and his wife come to see me and Linda whenever we first got married. One night ... Linda has heard this story several times, too. Heard them tell it one night. They was setting on the couch and I said, Ben ... There's a lake right out here called Guthrie. You know where it is, Daddy?'

'Gutherie? I've heard of it. I've never been there.'

'Well, I been out there several times. You go out there to Guthrie Lake and that lake stays full of water nearly the year round. Real pretty lake. It's fed by a little spring.

'One night Ben ... him and me was here in town ... I'll just tell you the whole story. And he said, Curtis, go out with me to the lake and let's pray to the devil. He said, Tonight he'll appear because it's full moon and it's right overhead. Said, He'll be there.

'I said, Well where he is I ain't. That's just what I told him. I thought he was crazy.

'I said, You're the silliest thing I ever heard of!'

'He's *still* crazy!'

'Another night or two ... he told me ... I said, Did he appear? Yeah! Come out there and told me what to do this week.

'So, his wife and him got married. They was over at the house one night and I said ... her name Emily?'

'Eva.' Linda answered.

'Eva? I says, Eva, does Ben still pray to the devil? And she said, Yep. Said, I didn't believe him, Curtis, whenever me and him got married. Said, He told me about that before we got married and I didn't believe him. And says, One night he told me he was going out there and pray to him. Said he'd prove it tonight. Said he'd have some *birds* come and appear to me at the door. And she said, Sure enough, while I was washing dishes there was two birds walked up there and knocked on the door.'

'*Walked* up and *knocked* on the door?'

'She said they was as tall as a man!'

'That was probably Ben and some crony!'

'Naw! He was in the livingroom, she said. And ... wait ... did she say they *talked* to her?'

'I don't remember her saying they *talked* to her.'

'I think it's enough to have a *tall* bird!' I started laughing.

'Get a tall enough bird and he don't have to do anything else!'

'She said she didn't *deny* his word anymore!'

'I don't believe I could've *lived* with him after that!' Aunt Maxine said.

'I don't believe I could live with anybody that (laughing) has *birds* for friends!'

'It's hard enough when drinking buddies show up!'

'Well, *I* couldn't live with anybody that prayed to the devil! That's *horrible* to think about! Ain't it!' Maxine insisted.

'He don't do that anymore. He told me that he wished he never had fooled with it!'

'Yeah.'

'That's like those people raising people from the dead. You hear of that? They tell me that's going on pretty strong in California! I heard it on TV here the other day!'

'Let's just hope they're making the right choices.'

'Who'd be the right choices?'

'It'd be awful to raise somebody from the dead and find out they were boring and you didn't like them after going to all that trouble!'

'People don't think of the *devil* being powerful enough to raise somebody from the dead,' Curtis refused to lose his leeway.

'You think the *Lord's* raising 'em up, Curtis? You think the *Lord's* raising them from the dead?'

'Well, he *can*. He *is*! But he's not raising them like the *devil* is!'

'What town were we talking about where you said, Where did all those people come from?'

'They raised them from the dead?'

'New York?'

'In New York I always feel like they've just got people stacked on top of each other.'

'Idn't there an awful lot of traffic in New York?'

'Yeah.'

'I'd like to *see* that town but I wouldn't want....'

'Jessie, you believe in that kind of stuff? Like that raising the dead and all that?'

'Naw. Do *you*?'

'I don't *believe* it! I *know* it's a fact!'

You feel like ...

'You feel like driving, Mama? You want to drive?'

'Don't make any difference, honey. Whatever you want to do.'

'Put your stuff in the back of the car.'

'She's been doing all the driving.'

'What you got your hairnet on for?' Maxine asked Mae.

'That wind's just whipping around out there. The minute I get over here ... between the wind and the moisture my hair just goes like a bush heap.'

'I think it looks real pretty.'

'I washed it and put it up over at Ethel's.'

'Tomorrow's my day to get it done.'

'It looks real nice.'

'I'm sure proud of those peas, but I feel bad taking your first....'

'Don't feel bad cause I've had ... Pearl brought us....'

'Peter said they could of picked a bushel in five minutes....'

'... and canned up a bunch....'

'I wish I'd of known they was over there. I'd of got them to take some paper bags. I'd of took some home and put them in the deep freeze. But these'll make two or three good messes, won't they?'

'Those? I don't know.'

'Jessie's proud of that stalk of cotton. As soon as she gets to the California border they'll take it away from her.'

'She could put it in her suitcase.'

'If I was her I'd put it in a plastic bag and shove it under the car seat.'

'Jessie, you better put that stalk of cotton in a plastic bag and stick it under your car seat.'

'I just put it in the trunk....'

'Naw, I mean for when you cross the California border. They'll take it away from you.'

'They'll have to fight me for it. That's valuable property with cotton going at three hundred a bale!'

Settling in.

I slammed the door with my left hand and leaned forward to look through the windshield.

Mama arched her back to pull her skirt straight ... then settled, smiled brightly through the glass.

So did I.

We pulled out of the driveway, waved into the vague air at them, still standing there, manipulated a few streets and turned onto the highway, going West.

Frenchy and Cuban Pete

Frenchy and Cuban Pete

In 1947 Albuquerque got its first stripper club. That was a good year for Albuquerque. The first Jewish Delicatessen opened on Central Avenue right downtown. And a lot of a very different kind of person started going to the University of New Mexico on the G.I. Bill.

The G.I. Bill changed the look of Joe College U.N.M. drastically. A large part of the influx, particularly in the painting department, were Jews from New York. That look blew me over. Everytime I saw somebody looking great it turned out later that he or she was a Jew. For awhile I got worried about it. That all my friends were Jews. Then I thought what the hell go along with it.

I sat through evening after evening of conversation so abstract that the only thing clear was that they all knew what they were talking about. And it was fascinating. You have to realize that the talk I had been understanding wasn't worth the effort. A presumptuous snob at seventeen is what I was, out of desperation. What these people were talking about involved rampant energy, arms waving, real anger for intellectual reasons and a dynamic. They were so knowledgeable. One of them who wanted to make love to me but we never did gave me a Modern Library copy of Sons and Lovers for my birthday.

I mean I was getting so much sustenance that not being able to follow the mesh of the reasoning and not recognizing the names of the heroes was trivial; hardly to be thought of. And there were consistent small bonuses like eating my first hot pastrami on rye.

Anyway, to return to the history of that city, that was then a growing town, that's supposed to have been the first year the Mafia made their move in on the overall action. It was a stripper club west of town, out Central heading for the desert.

The building was a junker; cement block with patterns. Inside, the room was a huge barnlike square, with a dance floor orchestra section intruding off one wall so the tables were jammed into the remaining three sides.

Every couple of hours there would be a floor show. The exotic dancer was naked on her left side with a little pasty on her nipple and a g-string. Her right side was dressed up like a red and black devil. She was split right down the center and the act was watching the right side get it on with the left side. A lot of the time it really looked like two people, the right side being agressive, the left side fighting it off, but being progressively overcome, even attracted. Hitting the floor at the same time and working up to a grand climax with all the lights going black to give her / it a chance to get up and walk away. Save the image from a tawdry exit.

And then Cuban Pete and Frenchy would come on for a comic turn. Cuban Pete was a short fat Greek with a mess of black curls and an accent. He wore a straw hat and a blouse with huge ruffled sleeves. The straw hat worked as a hand prop. He'd take it off with a flourish, give it a shimmy-shake at the end of his arm to make a point, and to enter, and to exit. Frenchy was six feet tall with a high bleached pompadour and spike heels, and almost nothing else. She was a walking example of what was legally allowed. She would station herself like so many pounds on the hoof in front of the band microphone as if she meant to sing. Thank God she never did. Cuban Pete would have a hand mike with yards of cable to let him meander among the tables while they went through their act.

They were really rotten.

The jokes were so bad that the only way you knew when one was over was the band would go 'Ta-Taaaa!' Then we'd all break up. 'Ta-Taaaa!' was the real punch line. It let you see where you would have laughed if it had been funny.

One of their routines was Cuban Pete would be out among the clientele yelling back, 'Hey Frenchy! How you like that movie I take you to last night?' 'Oh!' she'd say, her nose like a trumpet, 'Clark Gable was wonderful!'

'How you like that?' Cuban Pete would ask us. 'I say how you like that movie I take you to last night and she says Clark Gable was wonderful!' He would try again. 'Hey Frenchy, how you like that movie I take you to last night?'

'Oh!' she'd answer, 'Clark Gable was wonderful!'

'How you like that?' throwing his arms wide in mock despair so the ruffles would ripple.

'I want to ask you just one thing.'

'What you say?'

'I want to ask you just one thing.'

'She wants to ask me something. O.K. Frenchy. What you want to know?'

'I want to know if you're jealous of Clark Gable?'

'How you like that! I ask her how she like the movie and she wants to know am I jealous of Clark Gable!'

A long pause to build suspense, then –
'You gah-dam right I am!'
Ta-Taaaa

There was another routine that Frenchy walked or rather marched through with two other women. The orchestra played a rousing medley of *Over There* and *I'm a Yankee Doodle Dandy* and such like songs, and Frenchy would come marching onto center dance floor with a Marine's hat on. The other women represented the Army and the Navy. All three of them wore red satin brassieres and very short blue and white striped skirts. They marched into a triangle with Frenchy out front, all of them keeping a time-step, marching in place. Then the two girls in back marched toward each other and wheeled in unison toward the bandstand where they came by an enormous American flag which they opened out to make a backdrop for Frenchy. They marched around her wrapping her in the flag. The highlight was when all the lights went out and the flag and costumes glowed in the dark.
Ta-Taaaa

I did have a lover at that time. He was studying acting. I was studying painting. He would talk to me like two artists talking together.

He was also really tender. I had had an abortion three months before and I was basically scared about making love. I also had the Texas-Baptist blues riding hard on me ... down the drain ... seventeen and used up ... etc.

It wasn't the idea of getting pregnant that scared me, though that was certainly there. It was more like feeling raw and misused in my spirit and my body, and he helped me over that. It was a real piece of luck for me that somebody that decent and good-hearted happened along just then.

He used to make toasted cheese sandwiches with apple jelly spread on the top for us to eat in bed, talking.

Anyway, sometime along in there I started knowing the vocabulary and hearing the repetitions and one night at two in the morning some type, in the self-righteous tones we all know to our sorrow, said 'You've got to qualify your terms,' and I started crying and couldn't stop.

For a month or so I couldn't stand groups of people but then I gradually regained my perspective.

You know the brainwash goes that loss of innocence is a one-timer and thereafter you're left sadder and wiser. But in my experience it's cyclical; the place like the San Andreas Fault where your life makes a necessary dimensional shift.

And it's not such a loss, more often it's a trade.

And the pain of it is the least interesting thing about it.

The Boyfriend

I telephoned my mother on Christmas Day and she started right in telling me about her new boyfriend.

'He's another one of them damned Leos! All he wants to do every three or four in the afternoon is get in his old pick-up and tear around town!'

She said she met him when she went with Ed and Ella Lawney to their ranch for the weekend.

'Ella told me, "You just watch. He's going to be over here just as soon as he sees our smoke rising." They'd been filling him up with stories about me. We got there around suppertime and sure enough he was there inside of ten minutes. We all talked for half the night. We talked all through supper until four in the morning. I haven't talked like that in years.'

I remembered the Lawneys well.

They were neighbours of ours when I was in highschool. Ed Lawney drove a Singer like it was a sportscar and wore dacron slacks. He was strong on the surreptitious eye. Ella was jolly and very short and very fat. Having a husband with a taste for flashy style must have created domestic problems.

'He's after me all the time to lose weight,' she said.

Every day she would come to my mother's house and ride the Exercycle in the livingroom while she watched her favourite soap opera. For half an hour Monday through Friday the machine would move her through bicycling motions. The electric motor raised and lowered the handlebars like a rowing machine at the same time it turned the pedals around and around. The top half of her body shuttled back and forth, hands holding tight, while her knees pumped up and down.

The machine had two speeds. Every morning Mrs. Lawney pedalled and shuttled at slow speed for twenty-five minutes, then went to top speed for five, a stationary flying finish. She talked non-stop, her eyes on the television image.

'Lots of men take second jobs. Ed could easily work weekends, but no, he thinks it's *beneath* him!' Mr. Lawney was the principal of a highschool on the other side of town.

They had two children, a tall boy of eleven and a girl, four. The little girl was always lost in her clothes with the crotch of her underpants hanging to her knees. Mrs. Lawney made a point of buying children's clothes large enough to be worn-out instead of out-grown.

'Eddy wore his training pants until he was nine years old,' she would say.

'He says what if some of the parents came in and found him there selling shoes,' knees pumping up and down. 'It would *embarrass* him. He doesn't give any thought to me. I can work at two jobs alright. I do my housework and then I type term papers. *That's* not beneath him.'

And then she said, 'He's worse since he had his head operation. Now I guess I'll *never* be able to get him to take a second job.'

'Head operation?' I asked.

'They found a cancer on Ed's head,' my mother explained.

'He's so stubborn now. Since his head operation if he doesn't want to do something he just won't even talk about it. I say, "Let's at least *talk* about it. Maybe we can work something out if we just *talk* about it." But he won't even *talk* about it. And his temper's just terrible. When he gets mad he'll just yell as loud as he can. He just stands and screams at me. I get so nervous that the only thing that can calm me down is I go in the kitchen and I just eat, and eat, and eat,' a dreamy expression on her face, cycling along her private highway.

Now it's years later and in the interim there's been a success story and a happy ending, the cancer a thing of the past, a ranch for the weekends. The kids must have grown into their clothes and worn them out by now. It all worked according to plan.

'What did you talk about?' I asked.

'He said "I like a woman that's honest," and I said, 'Well, I can give you that on a platter." Then he said, "And what I *don't* like is a woman that goes after a man for what he's got," and I said "You don't have a thing that I want."

'I just told him, "I've got a monthly income that's as much as I'll ever need and a house that'll be paid off in six months and a three-year-old Buick that's in brand-new condition with only twenty thousand miles on it. Now just exactly what do you think you've got that I want?" And when he went to open his mouth I said, "Just shut up. I don't want to hear about it." Ed and Ella just hooted. I knew he was getting set to talk a lot of sexy stuff.'

I used to think a time would come when my body would turn me loose. Then last summer my mother and my Aunt Eunice came to California for a visit and got into telling stories on their friends.

'Well, you know how boy crazy Thelma Duvvelton is,' my mother said, 'She gets a facial and her hair fixed every week and goes to those old senior citizen dances and falls in love with anybody that'll look at her. She was even sillier than that when she decided to get married again. She went all the way to Alaska and didn't come back with a man.'

Both of them were breaking up with laughter over the stories.

One woman, when her husband died, wrote off to a man she had met and liked fifteen years earlier. He wrote back and they decided to get married. He wrote her that he was going to buy her a new car and drive it across country for her wedding present. She told all her friends about how she was getting a new Buick and she got a permanent and went girlish, waiting for him. But when he drove up it was a Chevrolet and she got so mad that she just sent him back.

'He knows I'm not interested in jumping into bed with him. The other night he was here and he said, "Honey, I've just got to leave. You drive me crazy."'

I can see her at the other end of the line, her head lifted at an angle, a tone of pride and humour in her voice.

'Well Mama,' I asked, teasing her, 'Are you sure you want to let yourself in for all that trouble?'

She went flat serious. 'You ought to see him. He's just as cute as he can be.'

A Special Condition

A few days ago driving over the mountain to do chores in Mill Valley Tom Clark said, 'When I came back from the hospital it took me just two or three days to realize that I had to get well fast or get sicker.' He was talking about walking around shrouded in a 'special condition.'

'Nobody could see me without going into the state of my health. It was really a drag, you know. It was really dull.'

What we had been talking about was Alec and Mary and how you can't see Alec without ... everytime you see Alec, even if he's laughing, you know he's miserable. If he's laughing you laugh with him, not to break his attempt at happiness. You're prepared to understand whatever he does. Special Condition Wipeout.

Mary talks more about it and invites a more nuanced conversation, and that's the tone of where *she's* at, and where *you're* at is as if you were knowledgeable, as if you knew Life and could tell her something significant. It's even as if she's asking you to.

With either of them you can talk about anything at all, houses, children, intentions; anything can be as if it were the topic.

Go through all of it. Do it all, everything you can think of.

All that grappling and swaying and the hands holding onto whatever comes in grasp like those comedies where the lights go off and everyone is yelling, 'I've got him! I've got him!' And when you look, all that energy disposed into the void, all those confusions paid dues on, and the rewards however fractured and slight now to be tabulated; what have you got but yourself again.

We make a mystique of it, therefore, having it to provide for. We call it some kind of seeking for self-knowledge. We speak of 'continuing to grow,' as if we'd meant all along that circuitous route to return to ourselves at the end. Not even a return; we say 'Ah, now I see I stayed here all along but how the vista did open.'

How we variously look for love, all of us, not actively even, rather, we stay prone for its happening. Think of all the religious nuts who waited and wait for God's touch as the 'blessing' they can propose forward of themselves in time. That is, their philosophy provides for it. Who better, for them, than God. He sees the sparrow fall.

Longing to have somewhere some thing registering more than its own encapsulation, wanting more than ourselves.

Wanting the abundance we grow given someone else's hands. And we do it too, for the other. We watch the other become substantial. We are each other's proof.

Then, when love 'dies', all that flurry occurs, because how can we let it go quietly, what was so significant, without marking its going down.

I Dreamed Last Night

I dreamed last night that I was living in an amalgam of places I've known well.

The house was at the end of a street, across the street from the Wades who used to live in Placitas. In my dream there was a sign on their house that said 'WE'VE TRIED PEACE. NOW LET'S TRY WAR!' Mrs. Wade had asked me earlier in the day if I had noticed the sign. She didn't think it was getting enough attention. It was a reversal as: Peace is what we've called War.

I remembered when I saw the sign that she'd asked if I'd seen it.

I went for a walk, turning right to go into the bigger collection of houses and I was thinking how *happy* I was, really feeling it, to have got it all together at last. Off to my right and about three blocks over would be the Foreshore in Belize with small sailing boats moored and rocking. There's been an improvement. No more buzzards. When they changed from direct current to alternating current all the buzzards were electrocuted during the next rainy season. They'd settle on a wire and rest back, their wet tail feathers would touch the other line and ZAZ.

And *really* the house I was living in, last night, was the house in Bolinas. I do feel closer here than anywhere else to the way I felt in Belize. It saved my life. The ocean is nearby and it's easy to be with people you care for. It's a kind of feeling open and in company in moist air and sunshine.

But the house *looked* more like the house we lived in in Placitas. It was down on the highway with a tin roof, and cramped. I registered some changes we'd made in it. The front porch was fancier and there was a garden with a California feeling to it.

It's hard not being able to pull it together. To drop off those bits of ghost into your history so that even as you think of those places the thought includes yourself, still there in your memory.

Sometimes those memories bounce out at you as if they had got powerful enough to conjure *you* up instead of the other way around.

But *really* you're here, in *real* time. A good thing, too. You can count off one-arm-one-arm-one-leg-one-leg. At least I never left any pieces of myself that stayed there, caught in the story. Unless you count what goes down in time, that we grow older and change, that way. And, of course, there's 'I left my heart in San Francisco.' And I did leave my tonsils in Texas. And there is a kind of romance about where we left our various innocences. But that was more often than not a trade.

In my dream I was very practical. The cat started having kittens and I got a big bucket of water to drop them into. That's the easiest way, supposedly, to be rid of new kittens. You just reach over and drop them in, never looking. And later you empty the pan into a stand of weeds. If you're tidy you can pick the bodies up then and put them in the garbage in a baggy.

Actually, it wasn't a bucket it was a large pan I boil vegetables in. I regretted not having something more neutral, anticipating in advance that I would remember the kittens when I used it.

The children were excited about the kittens and I hid the pan of water. They weren't to know. A harsh fact. It would all have been easier if they hadn't been home at that particular moment. But maybe I could do it the next day and say they had all died naturally, some disease.

In fact she only had three kittens and I was won over, abandoned my dream murder, thinking: In Bolinas we can easily get rid of three kittens; meaning give them away.

There was one more thing in addition to the kittens, the house, the sign, and the walk that let me have the experience of all my places being one and me in it. There was a really lewd baby boy someone brought by, who stared into my eyes and began to grow, meaning to get big enough to make it right off. I was holding him and in no time he was a child, then too big to hold, but only up to my waist when I put him on the floor. Continuing to grow, looking up into my face.

That's all I remember of that part. There isn't even a confused image of anything further happening. The growth and the intention seemed to be the point of it.

I Owe You One

Before it gets lost into the void I want to tell about a letter that got written to the Denver Post years ago. It could have been as long ago as 1947 or 1948.

It was apparently written in answer to a letter that had been written earlier and, judging by this letter,the earlier one seems to have been written by a woman who was complaining that when her husband got drunk he'd knock her around.

The woman who wrote the letter I read said that she had had the same problem.

She said she only weighed about a hundred pounds and her husband weighed close to two hundred pounds. She said for years he'd go out on Friday night and Saturday night and get drunk and then he'd come home and beat her up, then he'd fall asleep on the bed with his clothes on.

There came a night when he beat her up and when he had stopped she said, 'I owe you one.'

When he fell asleep she went outside and brought in a piece of two by four and she started pounding on him with it.

Of course, he woke up right away, and he beat her up again. And she said, 'I owe you one.'

She said that in no time at all she had him afraid to go to sleep. Then he began to see that it was O.K. to go to sleep if he hadn't beaten her up. So he stopped.

Considering the number of years it had gone on the stopping was really quick.

She said she hoped that her own solution would encourage the other woman to look for a solution because it was not hopeless.

The two principles involved were consistency and perseverance.

Free State of Winston

To start off with I was raised up in a family of nine. I was the *middle* one. That's a bad place to be Boy I tell you! I had two brothers'n two sisters oldern me and two brothers'n two sisters youngern me. I was in a fight with *somebody* ever day of my life.

I was *raised* in North Alabama in Winston County which is known as the FREE STATE OF WINSTON. When the South seeceded from the Nawth, Winston County seeceded from the South! So that whole *Wah,* anybody tawkin about *that Wah,* well, *we* didn't have no part of that wah. *We* seeceded from the South!

There's a big ol *cave* up there, justa little opnin about the size of *that,* well, acourse they sent *reecruiters* up there to git'm. They just shot em ever time they showed in that opnin. They couldn't reecruit em; they couldn't take em. They just *fired.*

Man there called Peglag Pike. Lost a lag y'know'n had a peg on. You ever seen a peglag? Ol' Peglag he had a place out of town about five miles, made *whiskey* there'n used to come in to town to sell it. Well, he come in to town one day, a case of whiskey on him, met the Sheriff. Sheriff went to kiddin him, said 'Peg, you got a license to sell that stuff?' He was just teasin him. Peg said, 'Yeah, I got a license. You wont to *see* it?' Sheriff said, 'Sure, I'd like to *see* that.' Ol' Peglag reached in under his coat, hauled out a forty-five with a barrel that long, said, 'You wont me to *read* it for you?' Sheriff said, 'Naw, just wonted to make sure you was legal.'

Well, two boys took to sneakin into Peglag's still and drinkin his whiskey when he wadn't there. He left a note for them said, 'DON'T DRINK THIS WHISKEY. IT WILL KILL YOU.' Well, they went on partyin there whenever they saw him head into town. So he left one day'n circled back around'n shot'm both down. One of them was sixteen and one of them was seventeen. So then they just didn't have any choice. Sheriff took a posse up'n killed him.

One of the women had just started using rouge and lipstick. Of course everybody in town, they just thought, well, all the *women* in town just thought she was the *worst* in the world! She'd come into town all painted up and sure enough the menfolk sorta shined up to her.

Well, the women wouldn't stand still for it. They just *had* to go do somethin about that. That was back in Kew Klux days. So finely the men just had to give in for some peace. They all put their sheets on, loaded up in an old Model-T Ford and went out on a clear bright moonlight night. They went up onto the porch and knocked on the door. Told her husband they wanted in. Well, he didn't mess around. He just took a double-barrel shotgun and let it off right through the door. Kilt the lawyer, wounded the doctor, god knows how many more. All the rest of them lit out straight back to town. Left the car and all.

They had to send somebody out there the next day to get a list of the dead and wounded.

Old Security

When Sarah started college I started getting mail from insurance companies addressed to 'Parents of Sarah Creeley.' They were giving me options on Sarah's potential demise as if being a freshman meant life-and-death strikes again, the biggest graph of all.

Ten thousand dollars was the sum most often mentioned. Some kind of mystic choice masquerading as rational. Like a number that stands for infinity.

Old Security Life in Milwaukee, Wisconsin enclosed a reply envelope addressed to their 'Youth Marketing Division.' Their letter started 'ACT NOW!'

True enough. Youth flies into the past even as we speak.

The letter said, 'Dear Parents: The dollar today does not buy what it bought yesterday.'

It's like the math game section in Scientific American.

'The dollar today does not buy what it bought yesterday. However, our Life Insurance Policy is a product that yesterday's dollar can still buy.'

That's for those of us who didn't spend yesterday's dollar the day before yesterday.

Under the heading of 'Provisions' their ten thousand dollar policy is called *Term* Life Insurance up to the age of twenty-five. After the age of twenty-five it's called *Permanent* Life Insurance. The main difference there is that *Term* costs you $24.00 a year but *Permanent* costs you $130. I think that's only fair. You get what you pay for. Apropos Life, *Permanent* has it all over *Term*.

'Even in an inflationary environment true values exist,' is the way they put it.

Don't make the mistake of thinking that kind of distinction doesn't count. Language can kill you.

There was a linguist named Whorf who worked for Insurance Companies for awhile. His specialty was finding out where accidents were caused by language. For instance, he was called in on one job where a factory was having recurrent explosions.

It seems that when the workers took breaks and smoked cigarettes out in the factory yard they all went to the left side of the yard. The right side was stacked with drums of industrial oil and there was a big sign that said 'FULL'. The workers were smart enough to not light up around all that oil. So they went to the other side where used drums were stacked under a big sign that said 'EMPTY.' The fact being the obvious one that the empties were full of gaseous vapours just waiting for a match.

Getting back to Old Security's *Facts to Consider:* 'The proposed insured's future is Now!' Which sounds somehow like 'yesterday's dollar' turned inside out. The reason 'Now' is so important is that Old Security is making life insurance 'available to the proposed insured at an age when most can qualify.' I guess that's a delicate way of saying that they're as far from dying as they'll ever be.

Those subliminal double plays are endless. One night Sarah and I were in the kitchen more or less watching a medical show on T.V. while I pasted up a collage on the kitchen table and she put together a circular jig-saw puzzle on a foldout card table.

The plot ran like this:

A young woman who is going to be married goes to a surgeon to have a mole removed because Bo deserves the best and when he gets her that's what he's going to get. The young woman's mother, a nervous, fashionable lady, comes with her because she and the surgeon are old friends and she wants him to remove the mole because Cissy deserves the best ... etc. Cissy also needs the standard blood test and a general physical. During all that messing around the surgeon finds a lump in Cissy's breast which is cut into after a lot of by-play and it's malignant.

The big question at this point is how is Bo going to take to a one-breasted bride.

And he takes it badly. He goes out to walk around the block and think about it. Cissy is pondering keeping her breast by having massive X-Ray treatments. If she does it that way she runs a much higher risk of dying. They make it look like death is desirable alongside being sent back to the store.

'Have you ever seen *one* T.V. show where a *man* facing life and death got hooked on a cosmetic issue?' I ask Sarah.

'What do you mean "cosmetic"?'

'Where the question of saving his looks was as important as saving his life.'

'No, I never have,' she said and got on with her jigsaw.

Bo decides to go with the loss and the plot moves into Phase Two.

Mama says she'll only feel secure if her old friend does the knife work.

Enter a young surgeon who has done a heart transplant on the old surgeon.

'Your heart won't stand it,' he says. 'I won't let you take the risk.'

It all starts to function like a variation on that nursery rhyme where the old woman is trying to get her pig over the stile.

The mother is persuaded to use somebody else.

The operation is successful.

Cissy is provided with a duplicate in rubber.

The happy ending is the young surgeon and the old surgeon walking into the sunset down a hospital corridor, both hearts beating a regulation number of beats per minute.

'Huh!' I grunt. 'They just mean to ignore the percentages.'

'You mean all those heart transplant people have died?' Sarah asked, looking shocked.

'Honey,' says I, 'It's even worse than that. All the people who don't have heart transplants die too.'

But back to Old Security. They have a P.S. on their letter about 'the advantages of independent decision, without pressure, made in private.'

Well, I'll buy that.

Twice

ONE:

Barry Hall told me that when they were living in Nassau there was a ship on the nearby ocean filled with a cargo of tapioca that got a fire down deep in the hold. They played water onto it but it kept smouldering, turning the water into steam.

When tapioca cooks it expands to eight times its uncooked size.

A time came when the crew abandoned ship and sat in little boats watching the tapioca pour out of all the ship's openings. Finally the ship exploded.

Barry said that for days afterwards there were gummy wads of half-cooked tapioca washing up on the beaches.

TWO:

A son who was a fisherman and had been going out in his father's boat finally saved enough money for a boat of his own.

The first time he went out with the fleet as his own man they had a fine turn of luck and came onto a massive school of fish. Everybody hauled fish in as hard and fast as they could. The son filled his hold and began to fill the cabins. It was a miracle.

The father radioed that he had a load and was returning home. The son said he thought to stay awhile longer.

The son was piling fish onto the decks.

Part way home the father got a radio message from his son, 'You'd better get our position. We're going down.'

Little Ernie

When we came back to New Mexico after the first couple of years in Buffalo our neighbours across the arroyo asked me, 'Well, how's about your famous cousin?'

'Who's that?' I said.

'Don't you know about Ernie?'

I have a cousin named after his father so he's always been Little Ernie to me. He was always a bright sharp kid.

For instance, he went along with me and a boyfriend of mine for a drive into the foothills once and while we meandered and did a little mild necking Little Ernie went around picking up tumbleweeds. I just figured he was hard up for something to do.

'I could sell these for Christmas,' he said.

It was early November but the sun was bright and clear the way it always is in New Mexico. Even when it's raining the sun shines. It was pretty much of an abstraction, a thirteen-year-old kid talking about selling tumbleweeds in a place where anybody can pick up their own. And getting into Christmas while he's sweating because the sun's so hot.

He filled the trunk and the back seat of the car with tumbleweeds to take home. He went back with other people who had cars to get more.

When he had as many as he wanted he spray-painted them gold or silver and hung a few little Christmas balls on them and sure enough, people bought them.

'It was in the newspapers! Didn't you read about it?'

It seems Little Ernie (except this was years later and he's taller than his dad, has been for some time but nobody shifted the names around) had gone into a military airfield somewhere and there was a jet fighter plane warming up on the airstrip. And Little Ernie climbed into it and took off.

He had never flown a plane before.

They got him on the radio and asked him what he had on his mind. He said he thought he'd go to Cuba. They sent two other jet fighters up after him and told him to turn around before they had to shoot him down. When they had explained to him how to turn around he did.

Then they told him how to land and he did that too. Just like a forties movie except that it was a jet.

They questioned him for awhile. He said he was an indigent insurance adjuster who wanted to start a new life.

This all happened before the hijackings or he'd have got a different treatment. As it was they just turned him loose and he went home.

Our neighbours across the arroyo couldn't believe that we hadn't heard about it in New York. It certainly made the headlines in Albuquerque. He was better than a local hero.

That whole family tended to be a little spectacular. Big Ernie looked like Anthony Quinn and had two hobbies. He always went on the yearly rattlesnake roundup in southern New Mexico, and he hooked pictorial rugs to hang on the walls.

The oldest boy, Sonny, saved up when he was about seventeen and bought a big-sized Harley-Davidson motorcycle. His first trip out on it he headed up into the Jemez mountains to visit his girlfriend.

According to his friends who were following in a pick-up he never dropped below seventy-five. And there were cross winds in gusts of up to 40 mph.

The obvious thing happened. He hit some gravel along the road and got slung high into the air and sideways into a cement culvert. The motorcycle smashed into a million pieces, but Sonny went through the only slit in the cement and got off with a broken leg.

They took him to a doctor who put a pin in it.

A week later deer season opened and Sonny went deer hunting in the Sandias. He slipped and rolled down a slope and bent the pin. He fired his rifle so his friends could find him. They took him back to the doctor who took that pin out and put another one in and a couple of days later Sonny got a deer.

When Big Ernie fell in love with a red-headed woman and took off, Little Ernie's mother and sister got their house declared off-limits it was so wide open. It was a kind of expression of grief on Little Ernie's mother's part.

The whole family was headstrong but Little Ernie took the prize.

Bathroom / Animal / Castration Story

This is a bathroom / animal / castration story.

Dianne and Drummond Hadley have a wildcat that was given to them by the guy that runs the Desert Museum in Tucson.

It stands maybe two feet high and is really substantial if you're used to looking at housecats.

It plays. If you pull a wad of paper on a string it plays. A little languidly but it's playing.

And the wildcat, as it plays, keeps its claws sheathed. And you get a little breathless from not really breathing normally and you get exhilarated with relief because every time the wildcat could jump you he doesn't. He just keeps batting the paper wads, almost politely, with his paws like mittens.

But when you look into his eyes you don't get further than the surface. He looks at you totally blank. No recognition of you, your organism, your species, nothing. When you look that creature in the eyes it's like there's no earthly reason for the two of you to be in the same room. It feels like you've taken off your shoes and socks and gone for a walk on a glacier.

When I went to the bathroom I realized the wildcat was as fast as it was supposed to be. I opened the door and the wildcat rushed to the toilet bowl before me.

Well, O.K.

I decided between two evils.

I decided not to put the creature out.

It was a lazy choice.

The cover was closed and as I reached to open it I saw that the wildcat was getting compulsive. It was pacing and jumping and generally acting nutty with all its attention focused on the toilet bowl. It was waiting for me to open the lid for some reason of its own.

I realized that there was going to be a skirmish with a winner and a loser. I knew which one I wanted to be.

I stood between the wildcat and the toilet seat. I blocked its every move while I did the necessary clothing stuff. I reached back of me and raised the lid keeping my eyes on the wildcat all the time. He went frantic. He rushed back and forth in front of me, trying to get past me, trying to look through me.

I won.

After I was seated he went really cool and uninterested.

Who needs it?

I stood up, flushed the toilet and wasn't vigilant. It seemed like there was no need to be.

The wildcat hit the toilet. He pounced his two front paws into the bowl after the disappearing water. Water flew to the ceiling. He pounced over and over. Water was spewing up onto the walls, the ceiling. I got soaked getting the lid closed.

He dug the game was over.

We walked out of the bathroom together.

'Why does your wildcat jump at the water?' I asked Dianne.

'Oh yes,' she answered, laughing, 'Men get really nervous.'

Dolores

Bob came home from going downtown in a rage, but keeping it rational all the way home, not screaming at the people in the streets, holding it in like a kid can fall and scrape its knee and run two or three blocks to get to mama before its voice busts out in a fresh bawl. Holding the knee in time to let it go where it counts.

'I was on the elevator in the bank building and I met,' he named somebody whose name I used to know but I'll never remember it again, Dick let's say for a tool to tell the story with.

'He was a friend of yours? You went to the University at the same time?'

That was true. I didn't remember much about him except that he was a wild neurotic.

This was nearly ten years later and I couldn't clearly remember what he looked like. All I remember about him is that when he got drunk at parties he used to chase his girl friend around with dangerous weapons. Anything he could get his hands on that was sharp.

Dick was prized for his high-strung bull-shit behaviour. It was like Art. We all felt pleased that we had to accommodate it. It was a forerunner of things to come.

We were all going to be great painters and writers and were eighteen up to mid-twenties. Neurosis was our bread and butter. It was as close as we could get. It's true some of those people still keep on but nobody made it big.

This particular party I'm thinking of is notable in my mind for two things: the host made it with four or five girls in the bathroom, one at a time, and somebody turned off all the lights as a way to keep Dick from mutilating his girl friend Dolores with a beer-can opener. Some people grabbed him in the dark, the lights were turned back on and they kept him in the kitchen and talked him into being calmer while Dolores stayed out of the way in the other room.

He only got really eccentric when he got really drunk. We were all intent on getting drunk. A lot of the conversation would be about who was in the bathroom throwing up and a lot of the conversation was about who was fucking who in the bathroom. The bathroom got a lot of play.

The next day I remember talking to two guys who were at the party. One was saying with admiration, 'He got five girls into the john,' and I say 'five?' and they suddenly both look worried and look at me, the eighteen-year-old with a big mouth who tells everybody everything, and one of them says 'Don't talk about it. It would really upset Amy.' So I said 'I won't,' and I didn't until now.

'Yeah,' I agreed to Bob's question. 'He was a nut. He used to chase his girl friend with knives and once he took off all his clothes and stood on a table and yelled that he wanted love and affection and he didn't care if it was a girl or a boy.'

That was the only other thing I remembered about him. We were all charmed by that, too. The combination of him stripping and his proposal of a 'girl or boy' was more than anybody else could get to.

I don't remember what his painting was like but we all felt that his temperament was exceptional.

'That's the story!' Bob yelled. 'That's the story that you told that caused his wife to kill herself!'

It's true his wife killed herself, and it was a shame. She had been really avid to go to school. She worked a part-time job for her tuition and books and supplies, and she waited tables in the cafeteria for her meals. She was pretty tough. And her painting showed a lot of work.

They got married around the time I did.

I left the States, lived in four other countries for six years, had two children, fell in and out of love, learned bits and pieces of other languages and forgot them, and returned to where I'd started for a divorce.

Dick and Dolores were still married. I saw them at somebody's house. He was working as a salesman. She was acting like a housewife. They had a couple of children. And a year after that I heard she'd killed herself.

Meanwhile, I got a job to support me and my kids and two years after my return I met Bob who, now, a year and one child later is saying to me, 'When you were in school together you told somebody that he took his clothes off and yelled that he wanted a boy or a girl and his wife killed herself at the implications.'

'It was a party,' I said to defend myself, 'there were thirty or forty people there. I didn't have to tell anybody. She heard him yell it, too.'

But it seems likely I told it to somebody. I loved to be living an interesting life.

Did somebody lay it on her so she couldn't stand the telling, so it was harder than that it had happened, and she mulled it over for seven years, living with him all the time and having two children as a side interest and then ...

I couldn't believe it. I don't believe it now.

I know how, in a lousy marriage, something can become the focus for your misery and it looks more like that.

I liked her and it somehow seemed that I'd added to her problem. I wish he hadn't turned into a salesman and she hadn't turned into a housewife after all those early guts.

Why didn't they go ahead for the splendid and make it come true?

And I realized that I couldn't defend myself in this conversation. I didn't know if I was right or wrong.

Bob was really bugged. This guy had waylaid him in an elevator and told him the tragic history he didn't want to hear, poured poison in his ear and sealed it off, and here he was home. Like a message from Garcia.

'It seems likely I told somebody that story because that's almost the only thing I remember about him,' I said. 'But I don't think she'd hold onto it for seven years before she killed herself over it.'

'Seven years?' Bob was dumbfounded.

Dick had made it sound like she heard the story and killed herself straight off. And my telling Bob the story as my identification of that person kept it all that immediate.

So that held in time too. It was a true coincidence. Everything converging to make this moment be a weird abstraction of who said what, caught in time.

'What did he look like?' I asked.

'Oh ... he was in a suit and a salesman's hat. He's married again.'

It was like talking about somebody we knew in common.

Bellagio

There is a place in Italy, a small town at the side of Lake Como with white buildings and curved red tile roofs; the doors and windows are deepset so that at certain angles they are black shapes in the white.

In some places the streets are so narrow that persons walking must press flat against the walls to let a car pass. In these streets unless it is high noon there is a black shade and driving along them there is a consistent flicker of the cross streets that extend like tunnels to the lake. At the far end of the cross streets Lake Como hangs half-way up the sides, a sheet of brilliant blue, suspended in perspective, and above it the paler blue of the sky.

This place figures in history. George Sand and Chopin came here, and Liszt with his lady love. Stendhal was a visitor as he could be. And much earlier, high up the mountain, in the very villa we are enroute to there is a cliffside where Michelangelo loved to sketch.

The car rises out of the maze of Bellagio to a higher edge of the town climbing the wedge of a hill into sunlight. It is a peninsula. All the edges to be seen from this higher centre touch water. And even from this higher vantage point there is a sense that the lake tilts, its farthest line reaching up.

The history of this place is an ambience of feeling. What caused those others to come here catches at oneself. I feel possessed by the charm of it. This is a charming place.

Pitches and Catches

There's a gap in the greater American consciousness about the low-downest level of the magazine business, and I'm going to feed a little into it out of my own true-life experience.

I answered an ad when I was seventeen that invited young women to travel in a chaperoned group and earn while you learn. For me the real hook was New Orleans. They were enroute to New Orleans, learning and earning.

I've always wanted to see New Orleans (and I still haven't. This isn't a story with a reasonable progression and an appropriate ending. It's just one more instance of oh, see what fits our foolish hopes.)

I telephoned and made an appointment to be interviewed at the Kiva Motel on Central Avenue. I got the job.

I can't imagine what might have disqualified me.

The job was selling magazine subscriptions door-to-door. That was how you earned and the learning had to do with the underlying principles of salesmanship. Within that simple and usual projection there were nuances so abstract that they could only be the outcome of bureaucratic thought; an inherent growth principle of crumby thinking.

For instance, one word you never say if you're a magazine salesman is 'magazine.' Pros peddle 'Books.'

When the lady of the house, that entrenched functionary, opens the door and looks at you and says 'I don't want any *magazines*' what you really start to work on is that piece of semantics.

We were handling Better Homes and Gardens *books,* Good Housekeeping *books,* McCalls *books,* Saturday Evening Post *books*; I mean there was just no way in the world to get around it, that we were peddling magazines.

And all we had to come against truth with, our naked faces looking able and our bodies on the line, our only tool against those hostile faces in the knowing world, was our 'pitch.'

We memorized the 'pitch' word for word. It was awful, just on the edge of literate with total non-sequiturs that had to be carried on pure voice alone, the eyes blank as if nothing had just gone screwy in the non-context.

I wish I remembered the damned thing. I'd give you the highlights. It was so eminently forgettable. In fact, that was a problem at the time. Every morning we congregated in one of the motel rooms and practised the pitch. It was so much an applied piece of goods. Take away the screen door and the lady of the house and the mind goes blank. The pitch disperses like gas, like any elective fantasy. So we practised it daily, to remember it, to put it into the day like substance. Then we went for breakfast. Then we were driven to the 'territory' and let out with our kits.

Well, I'll start at the beginning.

One morning early three new Mercurys stopped in front of our house on Byers Avenue and I came out with my mother's Samsonite suitcase. It and me were stashed in one of the cars and we headed for Arizona.

I was given a copy of the pitch and suffered the really expectable failing of seeing where it could be improved.

It was like coming up against steel. The pitch was not to be improved. The pitch was absolute. Questioning the pitch wasn't a question at all.

'It works,' the lady who had interviewed me said. 'We've got experts who don't do anything but come up with the perfect pitch that works and this is it.'

I started my training. I memorized the pitch. I went with the top peddler and saw how it steamrolled through objections. There were places that were pauses to let the 'prospect' speak. According to the objection made, you responded. And the only point of that little interchange was to get rid of the mounting tension that wanted to resist your salesmanship. The words it all took meant nothing at all.

It hurt me to see how the prospects went under. I didn't at all take it as a triumph. And in my heart of hearts I resolved that when they turned me loose I wasn't going to use the pitch.

I thought there must be a human place where I could stand and leave the person of the prospect unravaged. I believed that there were people who actually wanted to have subscriptions to magazines. And it was true that the rates we offered were the lowest going. I figured that with whole towns turning over under our crew I could depend on ratios.

That's how I learned at the age of seventeen that you can't underestimate human nature.

Straightforward and bare-faced I would start to outline the magazine subscriptions I had to sell.

I didn't achieve any one-to-one relationships. What I did was I gave a lot of people the opportunity for long overdue revenge.

You know the kind of expression you see on the faces of satisfied lynch mobs who mean to have their picnic now that the action's over? That's the look that followed me away down the sidewalk.

I was a magazine salesman who handed my body over. Boy, was I soft.

So then I started hating them, sitting smug, and me on my way back to the crew to hold down low man on the totem pole.

I started using the pitch. And it worked. I got a reputation among our little group.

It looked like I'd make a book salesman.

What I couldn't bypass was the moral torque. I was into an increasing anxiety. I was a hotshot acceptable criminal and the vanishing return on it was how I was tucking away subliminal guilt into bits of myself where I didn't have to pay attention. There was an accruing factor that earning money didn't touch.

We got to south Texas, still enroute to New Orleans.

One morning our boss gave us a pitch of her own on the value of poverty. The sense of it was that poor people are pushovers. They don't have muscles.

'Don't let the territory mislead you,' she said. 'I've had some of my best days in territory just like this.'

Because I was still new and it was another moral jog to be gained they sent me along with someone more experienced and I watched her talk a thin, ruined woman in a shanty into three subscriptions, complete with the first payment. The woman took three dollars out of a coffee can where they didn't have much company.

They put me out on a dirt road and the Mercury went flashing away leaving me standing in the swirl of its dust.

I sloped off across a sandy lot to a shed standing by itself in the blistering sun. It was the kind of arrangement where the top half of the front raised on hinges and stayed up with a stick, opening the place into a counter.

There was a stool and an old kitchen chair standing on the ground in front and I sat there all afternoon with an oldish Mexican woman, drinking Coke and learning Spanish.

'Hello.'

'How are you?'

'Good morning.'

'Good afternoon.'

'Good evening.'

I spent that hot afternoon rejoining the human race just outside of Houston.

We were supposed to have a treat that night. The Director for that area was going to take us to dinner at the Emerald Room in the Shamrock Hotel. We were going to hear somebody named Nat Brandywine play for a singer named Dorothy Shay. She was subbilled as the 'Park Avenue Hillbilly.'

I missed that reward, spent the evening packing, feeling alone and floppy. The bird had split the cage.

I didn't feel noble or even relieved. I just felt undefined.

I was really young, but of course I didn't know it then.

Don Cesar's Moral Tale

'There are two people lost in the desert. They have exactly enough water to keep *one* of them alive until help comes. What should be done?'

Don Cesar is a coldly handsome man with pale blue Sicilian eyes and white hair. Surrounded by his heirs he commands the room, has left his armchair to stand near the centre of the open floor. They must all look up at him from wherever they have seated themselves.

He raises his hand against the too ready answers.

'No! It is the *moral law* I mean! It is the *moral law* I ask you to consider.!'

He points at his youngest son, whose house he stands in.

'Tonio, you first!'

Whose face must assume an air of earnest consideration. Antonio twists in a pantomime of thought as a child might pose, scratching his head to make a show of thinking. His face gestures *thought*.

'Is there more water anywhere nearby so that the two men can get there by rationing the water they have?'

'You miss the point!' Don Cesar snaps in disgust.

His pointing finger circles the room, a moral dilemma.

The answers are questions. Are wives and children involved? Is one man much older than the other? Can one man take more than half the water and go for help?

Don Cesar grows more dissatisfied.

'If the two people are a man and a woman,' says Salvatore, called Beppi, who has arrived two weeks earlier from Italy to court Dolores-Rosa, and now walls his eyes at her, 'then the man should give up the water to the woman.'

It's clear that Dolores-Rosa agrees. Small and plump as a roasting chicken, her dark hair lifted into a great bulk of intricate curls, she approves him, smiling.

Don Cesar would shrivel them both with a glare on any desert if the choice were his but swings away from them, pointing along the line.

He is intent on the *right* answer.

To see Don Cesar walking was to recognize his worth. He carried himself rigorously, a man of pride and will who had not disappointed his own expectations.

He answered to no one. He was, himself, the proof of all his ventures. The Presidente owed him favours.

He was as certain of his own superiority as he was certain that his sons were less: less intelligent, less able, less healthy. He watched them carefully and was rewarded by exposing an assortment of laziness, carelessness, imperfection; there were always mistakes in what he entrusted to them. He despised them for being undermined so simply and not by a worthy opponent but by privilege. They were awash in a vague sea of gratification. They would never reach his measure. It saddened and reassured him simultaneously.

Meanwhile, he was exact. Tall and lean he cut a path wherever he went, as particular as a knife blade moving through stretched silk. He counted. No one could mistake him.

With his sons there was always reason for an edge of doubt. Their very appearance, their collective slouch, their dandyisms of dress could cause them to be mistaken for undistinguished gigolos or pretentious small-shopkeepers who dealt in Ladies' Fashions or Italian Guitars and German Harmonicas.

He was the current and they the gathering eddies that held what bits of wood and refuse happened their way. Dust settled on their surfaces in a fine film and around their edges a thin froth of scum accumulated. He could not understand them.

'There is *no* hope! There is no way out! The situation is no other way than I have told you! There are two *men*,' with a scornful look toward Beppi, 'in a *desert* with only enough water to let *one* of them live. What is the *moral law* to be considered in this instance?'

More weak mumbling.

The Christian and democratic consensus is that they must die together.

It is not good enough.

Sons, wives, daughters, suitor, they give him all the attention he demands. He is their future and still they cannot content him.

Dominick, the eldest son, his father's favourite, concedes that given a fair way to draw lots and an agreement between the two to abide by chance, one of the two, the winner, might live.

It is not good enough.

'The *law* of *survival*! *God's law*! The *first* law!'

The old man's finger is a rhetorical hammer.

'*God* gives you life! It is *criminal* not to *fight* to save the life that God gives you! The man who is strong enough to get the water for his own, that man *must* do whatever is necessary to survive! He would be going against God to die for a sentiment,' Don Cesar's lip twisted, 'for *sentiment!*'

His riddle ended he sits, without looking back, into the large chair that will always be there and his own.

Curry

I've been thinking today, planning a curry, of the sad little wife of the Major, ex-Indian Army, who did not cut her wrists when a very usual sexy female arrived to apply for an American visa and on that visit devoured the little Major as if he were a dressed-out partridge, but on the lady's *second* visit when the visa was ready and the woman rejected the Major in favour of the fat-assed U.S. Vice-Consul.

It was having her husband handed back as cast-off goods undid the Major's wife.

They were such dowds.

They could never have anticipated such a *romance* as that; the Major short and balding, his wife only one more of those incredibly dressed women once to be found in multitudes living their lives out in backwater British colonies.

The malice of that woman's choice, the dowdy major; and the ridiculous pathos of the later known stories, that the wife had bedded down on the couch to save them all from gossip.

In her happier or at least more felicitous days she taught me to make curry, and the last time I saw her (we were due to leave the following week) was at an official dance. The Major and his wife were in the Governor's party which meant standing, having to stand, at attention just inside the door while the band to announce the Governor's arrival played 'God Save the Queen.'

That arrival, her wrists taped so neatly it was decorative, and herself with her eyes straight ahead of her, herself standing at attention facing out into the room that faced back, a roomful of people who knew the story to some extent.

I went home from that dance alone, Axel having many young ladies to say his goodbyes to.

At the club Saturday nights I could say, 'Do you know who the most beautiful woman in the room is?' having watched him ogle the lot.

'That one?'

'No, that one over there, in the far corner, in the white dress.'

And he would look, as if hypnotized, to agree that yes she was the most beautiful woman in the room and move to join her company.

Poor Axel, he had almost no imagination.

For my own part, insofar as I remember it, my behaviour had something to do with an exaggerated notion of what passed for worldly. I was only twenty and it stands to reason that I believed myself to be sophisticated. It was a value in my mind.

A letter from Gordon says, 'How long ago it seems and I have no nostalgia left for those Belize days. Belize was too broken after Hurricane Hattie it was awful. We were not sorry to get away.'

And he says, 'Where you lived stood. Lindstrom's house was totally down and Sir Alfred was laconic and Lady L. mental, I thought, and quite funny and pathetic.'

And he says, 'Belize a monumental ruin.'

The only friends in my life were there, perhaps forever true, coming as I have to be so ambivalent that I must weigh every piece of cheese pro and con.

Still, if I exaggerate, the place and the people have changed. No one left to contradict or distinguish between the memories I stored back even as they happened, knowing I would want them later, *that* sadness in forethought, I loved it there, a kind of homesickness *in situ* as if I walked backwards. And the memories of *now,* rising up, that I didn't know I had. As that when I touched the Major's wife's wrists to say 'Did you hurt yourself?' she winced so deeply I was struck silent, remembering only then the bit of story I'd heard that afternoon, why her wrists were bandaged. Wondering, shocked, how I could have forgotten.

How could I have forgotten?

Old Vivvy

Roosters bring the day up, poor scrawny things to sound so splendid. Before the first show of light their racket begins. They excite each other to hysterical effort.

The dogs are also infected, that in the day's heat will have as much as they can do to move from the sun into the shade. They bark and howl until they feel they've done enough.

Old Vivvy, wearing a dirty rainbow of dresses goes into Mrs. Mac-Veitche's prized garden, a shadow among early drawn shadows, to pick the flowers.

'When that woman was a child ...' she owned the first piano in the colony. Her parents meant to make her a concert pianist. Both parents were killed in an accident and the child's guardian took the money. That was the story.

In the local voice, a calypso swing to her speech and with the drawn-out, pulled-out rhythms of any storyteller dealing with a myth, Rita says to me, 'Whan dat whomahn wass a chile ehveryting she touch wass *gol'*!'

Who stands now in the palest gray lift of early morning at Mrs. MacVeitche's door, a mahogany door polished to a high shine, and drops the brass knocker repeatedly on its sounding brass panel until the door is opened a cautious crack then wide by Mrs. MacVeitche herself, in a pink dressing gown, who looks in shock to see her treasured darlings, all the flowers from her garden, in a crushed mass, a madwoman's bouquet, held toward her as Old Vivvy simpering says, 'Fi' cents!'

Mrs. MacVeitche pays the five cents and brings her fresh-picked flowers indoors, to the kitchen, where she puts water in the sink and the flowers also. Flowers, she would be the first to say, are best picked in the early morning while dew still clings to the petals, as it does to these.

Vivvy takes her five cents and turns down Queen Street to go to the market.

The rising sun finds the day already begun in that small colony of houses. The roosters have crowed and stopped. The dogs have barked and stopped.

Old Vivvy, having been raised to be clean, comes to the Fort Square sea wall to bathe. The cast-off dresses she has been given, layers of filthy faded print, are laid across the wall. Wearing, on different mornings, one dress or two, or nothing at all (her body is younger than she seems with her tangle of hair and her lunatic face) she goes into the water among the floating garbage from that morning's slops.

Light pours horizontally over the flat still water and the day's heat begins.

Piece of Trash

He was a piece of trash from the first, not to be taken seriously. He arrived in the colony together with his wife, a heavy woman, and two daughters who were, one later learned, twins but not the identical kind.

They seemed good enough girls, quiet and formless, pre-adolescent. But the parents were, each in their own way, impossible.

The mother was graceless, with a raucous voice and a continuous line of harangue. She seemed never to stop. She had only to start again to erase any ease of quiet that had fallen since her last speaking. Peace was such a rarity in her presence that there was no enjoyment to it, one simply waited for the accident of it to be corrected.

But that was no justification for his being such a squirmy stick. He stood back of his wife's vulgarity inviting understanding. Now, what kind of man is that? The complacency of that immense self-pity of his, he believed himself to have deserved better.

What he believed he deserved was clear all over him, a kind of slime. He ogled all the girls from behind his wife's back. He was immensely capable of changing his expression whenever she had reason to turn his way. On and off he flashed according to the direction her head was turned. For her eyes he was proper and insignificant, gone quite into the woodwork. At her back he was wormy with pink edges around his eyes and mouth, as if his lips hung open, as if he panted.

It was no compliment to be looked at by him. One felt glimmers of his fantasies, ugly and trivial. A rotten kind of Hollywood sex-dream like those ads that say 'Learn to be a Hypnotist' and show some man looking potent and evil with his hands hovering over the unsuspecting breasts of some swooning female.

Anyway, there was a relief in knowing they weren't to stay in town but were almost immediately to go up-country. He was some kind of functionary for the Stann Creek establishment.

But before they could properly leave he wrecked his jeep on the one-lane road between the town and the airport and his wife was thrown right through the canvas roof and killed. One of the girls was badly hurt and had to stay for awhile in the hospital.

What was difficult was the necessity to show him sympathy for what so clearly was not a tragedy in his life but a release. He had believed she was the anchor that held him back. He was rampant to get on with what he thought was now open to him.

It's possible that in the way of fantasists he had convinced himself that all the women he lusted for reciprocated his fancy.

Instead of staying decently at home with his unhurt daughter he showed up at the club any evening he wasn't invited out to some commiserative dinner.

There were two clubs in the colony. One was very proper and almost exclusively white. Its only black member was a judge whose wife was now a faded lower-class white he had married in London while he was there as a student studying Law. The other club allowed anyone who could pay its fees. All the whites in the colony belonged to both and the good family mix-bloods and blacks belonged to the second.

It was the second club that the new-made widower frequented. He had a dated idea that the mix-blood girls were there for the taking, which wasn't true. In most cases they were strictly chaperoned, while the English or South African or Australian, in short the daughters of white colonizers, were let go almost casually and were endlessly boating or dancing or playing tennis or whatever without any supervision.

The more generous minded women interpreted his feeble attempts at lechery as 'Poor man, he can't bear to be alone. He simply haunts the public places for company.'

But even their good-heartedness was stilled when his need for company stopped showing itself at the clubs and he began to go nightly to the local dance halls.

His frustration, the frustration of at last getting into his imagination's Eden only to find no fruit fell to his hand shifted his search.

You must realize that this move on his part at that time constituted what could only be called going to the dogs. 'Men go *bad* in the Tropics' was one old English saying.

If his wife had lived he would probably have come and gone in proper order. As it was he had no sense of behaviour.

I don't mean who he took to bed or whether he did, I mean he had no notion of how to maintain appearances.

The prevailing notion was that all the whites owed it to each other not to go to pieces under the colonial strains. Pukka-Sahib was not a literary joke.

Of course, one only had to pay attention to such a sense of things if one wanted to maintain relationships with the other whites.

He hadn't much imagination but even so he realized quickly that his communication with the women-folk of his fellow civil servants was suddenly nil. All dinner invitations and the little attentions that showed he was one of a group stopped.

His daughter fortunately was not made a pariah on his account though it's hard to know how much she was aware of anything. She spoke almost not at all and was clearly in a state of grief for her mother and the sudden changes in what had been until now a quiet and usual existence.

The sister in the hospital got better and the small family left for upcountry but were back in a matter of weeks. The father had got amoebic dysentery and was himself hospitalized briefly in preparation for being shipped back to England.

They left on a Saturday afternoon on the weekly plane to Jamaica and my last sight of them was the two girls who didn't look alike going quietly and straightforwardly into the plane. Their faces then appeared, placed and ghostly, back of the round glass windows.

The father halted at the doorway and looked back, waved his hand as if to many friends, his fantasy still holding to that extent. He had no altered sense of his own worth though physically he had lost pounds and was as pale as if he had been washed in bleach.

Then he entered the two-motor plane to join his daughters and that was the last of him.

Why Does Anyone ...

Why does anyone write except to speak of those things that conversation will never elicit; what is closest to the heart. And to speak of the personal with some accuracy, in the proper setting. And to have finally and for once the statement of the thing, dear thing, caught out of the void, caught onto paper; to be there at least as real as what usually happens, namely that we are so often misshapen by event, obscured by misunderstanding.

I know how those papers flutter in every breeze, ephemeral. They are so fragile. Statement is fragile. It only exists as its record.

But the records of the heart return to the heart as information.

And we are so hungry for it.

Why does anyone write except to say what presses closest to them; what matters.

How Has ...

How has this nightmare come to usurp my life. Where did all that thought go that was so fine and as if life were available. Oh, of course it is. But once it seemed so simple and now it's so complex. I find myself in the middle of it and the mess of it as if I were another item in the chaos of it. No life at all.

It used to stem forward and I was the root of it and my life grew out from me and was my own.

It is true that too much despair for too long a time deprives the sensibilities of their assumption of hope. Discouragement strikes in the most trivial places that required no courage at all.

There is living in one's skin. The skin extends to include sunshine and those etceteras of daily pleasure. And just inside and within that coat of apparent daily possibility there is the great gaping torn thing that is life gone wrong. There is the thought as one is suddenly caught back from thoughtlessness, there is the thought that is a feeling that somewhere it has all gone wrong.

If there's a place I know not of, that is a place where I want to be. Does that necessarily mean that there is no place for me. And so we keep on. Just that fantasy, that one *can* think of a place for oneself, makes it as if it is there and waiting.

No wonder we go crazy. Not out of our heads but into them, where everything is provided for. Where we imagine the shape of our lacks and fill in the gaps and bring the furniture in and live there.

One wants finally to destroy the world as a mercy. How to be rid of the pain of it.

But in pain it is as hard to imagine simple pleasures and uncomplicated days as it is to remember pain during happiness.

And the rest.

There's An Old ...

There's an old Texas saying that I think I may be the only one who remembers it.

It goes 'I've enjoyed just about as much of this as I can stand.'

It's a magic formula that lets you head for the door past all the frenzy of any minute now it's going to get significant. It's a way to say that whatever you had in mind this ain't it. It lets you stop eating slop that needs a palate and a vocabulary.

I've enjoyed just about as much of this as I can stand.

It's A Phony

It's a phony surface but who's to know the difference. Not enough time. All that flash.

Hey, it's as good as real. Like living a life.

'Who said that?' drawing back and centring. Let's show a little muscle here.

'You saying this ain't my life?'

Naw, I never said that.

'I know what's real. I feel it.'

Yeah, we all do.

Got From Yeats' 'Celtic Twilight'

How Columcille cheered up his mother. 'How are you today, mother?' 'Worse,' replied the mother. 'May you be worse tomorrow.' The next day, 'How are you today, mother?', and the same. The third day the mother said, 'Better, thank God.' And the answer, 'May you be better tomorrow.'

(of Paddy Flynn) 'He was a great teller of tales, and unlike our common romancers, knew how to empty heaven, hell, and purgatory, faeryland and earth, to people his stories. He did not live in a shrunken world, but knew of no less ample circumstances than did Homer himself.'

(a weaver said) '... for there are three things that are the gift of the Almighty – poetry and dancing and principles. That is why in the old times an ignorant man coming down from the hillside would be better behaved and have better learning than a man with education you'd meet now, for they got it from God.'

The Dismay of:

Outside the glassed door, looking through, being on all fours, not to be seen; looking through the merest corner of the door, just an eye of mine and a corner of my upper right face in that lower left corner of the door; there I was *hidden* insofar as to be seen the other must be specifically *looking*. And the occasion was this, that she was going to come down the stairs and I meant to see just when, and how, and maybe follow the direction she went, or, perhaps it was *time* I was after, I wanted to know *when* she came down the stairs and went.

But what I saw was, at the point where the lowest stair pushed beyond the corner wall that concealed all the rest of the staircase, the corner where she would appear, walking past and down the one last step, leaving the stairs; there where her feet and lower legs would have been had she come walking, there was corner of face and one eye and a bit of vivid blonde hair and she was also crouched beyond the wall, on the stairs to look toward the glass door.

We laughed but it was a despair. It had been important that the concealment and the watching work.

Take Love, For Instance ...

How can it be desirable, that flurry of feeling that if it continues and maintains intensity we call Love?

How perverse we are relative to our own good to have that in our feelings that from the age of thirteen or so, younger all the time they say, until seventy or whatever, no end to it they say, we give over or are given into the 'divine emotion.'

Divine mix of anxiety, insecurity, longing that drives us until if we are fortunate, lucky in love, we have a brief relief that shines like fulfilment.

The constant fool's miracle, like fool's gold, but inherent; an inherent miracle. Passion brought to bear on eyes that shine back.

And then, or somewhat later, downhill all the way.

From here to there. Remember *there*.

Caught in the clutches of a one-way ticket. Express.

We are poor.
We are poor.
There is nothing here.

And we sling our everything into the void of it, to be caught.

What is that appetite that pretends to sustenance and ends with all the colour gone from the day and no one funny anymore. The appetite that carries veils and obscures our memory.

And can you in that moment's tender voice say No to it? How mean to refuse it, this little miracle that does so want in. Feel it knocking at your heart.

Poor heart.

See what followed me home.
Can I keep it?

Plan

or – do it with colour and light
a clear spot for the actual
voice, one colour for the
'definitive' voice, one colour for the
narrator. go black on return
after intermission – 'if you were
a desert bird' ... to ... 'mother ship'
colour rises overall *rose*

what about a tape with itself a
second time just off so the voice
is a stutter or echo throughout

circle those 4 statements
between the two screams

then *she* says, 'Son, I see ...

Some Bits

'Sweet dreamland faces, passing to and fro
Bring back to Mem'ry days of long ago.

Ted Berri-gram

Joanne's *range* as wide
as spread out on a table
and herself with a first-rate
boarding-house reach

grey eyes
GREY EYES
(her)grey eyes

She shrugged her shoulders and abandoned the personal side of the subject.

Actually we cannot put ourselves back into the spirit of those days.

A punitive spirit entered into our subsequent negotiations.

Soft and slow cartwheel of yourself sheathe your tongue walk in the true hot sunshine.

'You're so human ... You know what I mean, you always put your hand out to see if it's raining.' *Sido*

New Stories

The Elevation of Terre Haute is 50 Feet

When you come to Terre Haute's city limits there's a metal sign, a shape like the state of Indiana. And stamped into the metal you can read:

'Terre Haute Indiana pop. (so and so) elevation 50 feet. The birthplace of Paul Dresser who wrote The Banks of the Wabash.'

Terre Haute is one of those cities that flourished and grew a hundred years ago. Coal and steel exploded it outwards and surfaced the fronts of the main street buildings with a variety of fancy cut stone façades. The end of the First World War marked the turn. The city began to dwindle as its nourishment lessened. And now the beautiful stone faces that are still distinctive all have blind eyes. The windows have white or black or dark green painted on the inside of the glass.

Not enough people walk the streets. The women are in cotton house dresses. The men are in overalls and khakis. It looks as though this story was meant to be about a small farm town, and the set man got it wrong on the false-front buildings, too grandiose.

In the very middle of town the bulky courthouse and its lawn use up a city block. On one corner of the lawn on the mainstreet side there is a large statue, a memorial to the Civil War. Have you ever thought of that pun, the Civil War. There are four pedestals marking the four corners. On each pedestal is a representative warrior. There is a Confederate soldier, a Confederate sailor, and a Union soldier and a Union sailor. Steps climb between the four pedestals to the plateau that holds a tall column with a man on horseback high overhead. He is holding an unsheathed sword. He is a specific hero with a name. Metal chains drape between the pedestals to keep people off the steps. And from the exact middle of each chain hangs a small cleanly painted sign that says 'Please Do Not Spit On The Monument.'

When we were driving across country a couple of times a year I came to love Terre Haute Indiana. I decided to make a movie of it. Every time we went through I planned to take some footage. When we stopped in the business district to let me get a long shot of the street a man came out of his store, glared at me and my camera and conspicuously made a note of our license number. He was not to be fooled. When the caper came off he wouldn't have been slack.

Terre Haute was also the birthplace of Eugene Debs and Theodore Dreiser. The city made some choice to forget about them. Debs was too radical and Dreiser was indecent. He wrote dirty books and seduced young girls and got ruined by his excesses. But when Dreiser was born at 8:30 a.m. on August 27, 1871 'three graces garbed in brightly coloured costumes' entered the room and circled the bed. They were witnessed by his mother, his father and his sister.

He was the ninth child in a poor family in the poorest part of the town. His brother Paul changed his name to Dresser during the Great War. Dreiser was too German. Paul Dresser wrote *My Gal Sal*. He dressed in plaid suits and bowler hats and was a fine figure of a man.

But for the sake of the record it was not Dresser who wrote *The Banks of the Wabash*, it was his brother. The twisted lecher who could never look the other way, whose birth was attended by the graces, Theodore Dreiser wrote the words Terre Haute still holds in memory.

Oh, the moonlight's fair tonight along the Wabash
From the fields there comes the breath of new mown hay
Through the sycamores the candle lights are gleaming
On the banks of the Wabash far away.

Salamander

The tilt of a delta valley; this place is the Salamander, the great dish of the alchemist's, shelving to let its downward edge rest at the ocean's edge.

Where they meet there is a small line of beach. The sand reaches unevenly at the townside; there is seldom a clean line. A slow motion falling away of the cliff that is the dish tilting up and away from the beach causes landslides that dump downward to messy shapes.

Some years the beach grows to an almost impressive width as if the ocean brought sand from other places to give us a grand gift. Now there's real room for frisbee, more privacy for lovers. The children move farther from their parents. Things are more peaceful. There is more room.

And other years the sea takes it all away. One day it's there and the next day we find that overnight, in one great bite, our beach has gone into the sea, taken away elsewhere. I wonder, sitting on the few high bits that are left, who is using my beach now? Where did it go and where did they wake up this morning to find their world expanded. Or, that stupid and mindless thief of an ocean could as simply have piled it in places where no one has any use of it, the lee side of bridge pilings, islands where there isn't any water and no one goes.

Meanwhile, we are all on top of each other in these shrunk places, usually half-moon shaped, the result of earlier landslides higher and deeper into the land mass. The children are falling over each other, crying. The bullies have emerged and are feeling threatened that the territory must be redealt. They are solving it by winning. The losers are filling the beach with themselves as victims. The lovers have gone elsewhere or are modifying their behaviour. The great number of dogs that live here have become pests. When there was room for them they could take long romping gallops and come up to be with people as a place to lie down and snooze or simply check in before going back to their distant places. Now they shake water over us, throw sand on us.

Rats go crazy in congested space, and us, we also go crazy in it. The parents scream at the children to insist that the children stop. The children scream at each other. The winners are looking so disgusting I want to kick them. The victims are wailing in their dramas. It is intolerable.

Of course it is really not this bad. I am describing the bad part. And this is not a year when the sand is away. This year the sand is here, the beach stretches into distance like a Fellini movie. And this year the sun is shining and has been shining since May. It is so unlikely. We are blessed by a drought.

It is never *too* bad. It is quite tolerable, actually.

I have lived here for six years now. That is longer than I've lived anyplace since I grew up. When I moved into the house I'm living in now I had moved 23 times in 15 years.

This is my home.

I can't bear it. The notion 'this is my home' and my heart quakes inside me. My immediate reaction is to begin packing. But I hate packing. I will do anything else. I'll stay here and not call it home.

A Sense of Humour

I don't remember who said it but somebody said, in fact wrote it down in a book:

Sober people can't take humour seriously.

And it's true. If you're a writer you should know that you lose genius points with one whole set of people everytime you make them laugh. And if you really get to them and make them laugh a lot they may just give you up as hopeless and not to be counted on.

Critics of that persuasion will say things about you like 'not to be taken seriously!'

Mark Twain got the short end of that stick. Saul Steinberg. Make up your own list.

Those guys who opt for the miseries as what they can understand never have to worry about laughing in the wrong place.

Take that story we all know about the man who overnight turned into a giant cockroach and now he spends hours on the ceiling with his friends and relatives shoving garbage through his bedroom door. Not a laugh in the carload. That cockroach and his clan were humourless. Remember the endless why why why throbbing like an undertone. No sweet young thing to kiss that trapped piece of misery and turn it back into a dull and humourless young man.

It didn't have to be that grim and it didn't have to be to the death but dying comes easier to people like that than a good belly laugh. Killing off that poor cockroach was their kind of happy ending.

Mark Twain would have put a saddle on it, joined the circus, and made the family fortune.

I don't want to belabour this so I'll just close with something somebody else wrote:

Gravity is a mysterious carriage of the body intended to conceal defects of the mind.

Rosario

One problem with intelligence is that when it's thinking about something it thinks it's knowing something. And if it's mistaken and learns the difference then it starts thinking about it the new way and thinks it's knowing something.

When I was living in a little village in New Mexico where most of the people were Mexican and interrelated there was a man I'll call Rosario Rodriguez.

The thing about Rosario was, he was a crook. He was also a really good plasterer and bricklayer if you were strong enough to make him come through.

Everybody knew he was a crook.

When I moved to that town the word came all the way from Panama where a lady who had heard of the move wrote to say, 'If you get Rosario Rodriguez to do some plastering for you don't pay him until he has finished.'

One curious thing about that village was that a lot of the Mexicans there were Protestant. It stemmed from a really early time when that village had an argument with the priests in Bernalillo. The argument got so hot that the whole village went Protestant despite the fact that most of them had never even seen a Protestant. For a long time that village was known as the 'Pueblo de los Protestantes.'

Later on some of them turned Catholic again but a lot of them stayed Protestant.

Anyway Rosario was a Protestant. And at one of the church's business meetings someone brought up his case, that is, his being a crook. The gist of it was, 'Rosario is a crook because nobody trusts him. He has no pride in himself because he knows that everybody thinks he's a crook. If we gave him a reason to know that we trust him he would be a changed man.'

They decided to make him the Treasurer for the church.

When he stole the money everyone said, 'Of course, it was foolish to give the money to Rosario because Rosario is a crook.'

Doing Psychology

'I got the house, and I got the car.' (Which she tooled expertly out of the parking lot, holding the steering wheel with the pads of her hands, fingers extended, nails too long to be curled under.)

'Well, I *needed* it. I couldn't go looking for a job or go to school or do anything without my car! I sure didn't intend to just sit in that damned house and go loony. Not with *him* off on a honeymoon in *Bermuda*! And I got alimony and I got child-support. Me getting the house means the kids get to go to their same school. But that house really takes some keeping-up! And if I decide to sell it *he* gets half of the profit. How about *that*! I can *see* me doing *that*!

'Well, I never would of let him have the kids! He would have had a *fight* on his hands if he'd tried that!'

Her ex-husband had married his twenty-three-year old secretary and they had returned from Bermuda to live in a 'swinger's' condominium. Fighting for the kids seemed to me to be remote from his plans.

I asked her whether she wanted to be a writer. We were returning to the city from a reading I had given at the local University. She had attended with a group from the University's writing workshop.

'Oh yes. I don't know yet what kind of thing I want to write so I take all the writing courses. And *grammar*! I've been doing a *lot* of grammar. And *psychology*. I do a lot of psychology. Do *you* do a lot of psychology? I mean, *did* you do a lot of psychology when you were beginning? To get the motivation straight and stuff? It seems to me that your work has a *lot* of psychology in it.'

'No, not much. I like William James. And some Jung. Not like studying it.'

'*Carl* Jung!'

'Yes.'

'My *favourite*! I take from this professor that loves Freud. *Sigmund* Freud. He wants me to go to Europe with him on his sabbatical. That's next year. Vienna and Switzerland. What do you think of Switzerland and Vienna?'

'It sounds exciting. I've never been to Vienna or Switzerland.'

'You've *never* been to Europe?'

'I've been to some places in Europe. I've never been to Vienna or Switzerland.'

'Where've *you* been?'

'England. Holland. Germany. Denmark. France. Italy. Does he want to go to the Eranos lectures in Switzerland?'

'What's that?'

'The Jungians get together and deliver papers to each other on some topic.'

'Oh no. He just likes Freud. He wants to work on ... you *know* how Freud said everything is sex? You know about that? I mean, the *creative impulse*. Freud says that if you don't have enough sex it interferes with your *creative impulse*. Of course, there's two streams of thought on that. Well, this professor's interested in how it is the other way around. What happens to the creative impulse when there's too much sex? Well, maybe just *enough*! But does it interfere or what? What do *you* think? Do you think too *much* sex would interfere with the creative impulse? Or do you think it might help it along?'

'Hard to say. There are only so many hours in the day.'

'Yes, well *that's* true. That's an interesting way to think about it. So *we're* ... he wants me to help him research this *other* angle. The *too much sex* angle. He says that *nobody* has done hardly *anything* on *that*.'

Roots

Roots! That cry goes up that wants *My Story*! Where's *mine*? Where's the cigarette machine I was so casual about and the drug store that had a counter and how a gang of boys look on a gang of bicycles out for mundane adventure?

Where's my story?

How did it get cut loose and drift away down time and nobody even noticing it like continental drift across ocean floors and somebody takes wrong steps along the shoreline and falls into the water because the land has gone away...

Just like that the stories went away and people are getting hungry for them like a vitamin deficiency, that subliminal. And will the stories ever come back? The ones who want them are gathering like ancient tribes gathered when they saw they had lost their gods and now must call them from the shores.

There's a sense that that's why psychiatrists have proliferated. That's where the stories are let out now in bits and pieces and everybody's a learner, looking through the mystery of the bits to recollect them into entity and come by meaning. Poor Osiris, and all those daily dispersions, and all the disassociations we experience moment to moment now that war has made geography general. Now that home got stuck in time way back there with childhood and adolescence and yes sometimes I remember those long summer evenings in the halflight of late day returning home across grass lawns punctuated by driveways, eating, if I was lucky, a cone of raspberry ice cream.

The trees were large and old and went down when they widened the streets across this whole nation. Part and parcel with when the cars went big as a value. Big streets for big cars. That kind of trashy thinking where the exterior was suddenly the winner and got all the goods.

What in God's name did they think was going to come down those streets that needed that much room!

Forward thinking like the cargo cults put their little piece of landing strip in the middle of their home place and wait for the great silver gods that have gone into the sky and pass over their heads to notice. See, we have made a place for you dug into the body of our place and we wait, see we wait.

And the trees went down. And the houses that had been dappled with shade and private, each one a thing, they got dumped onto the street and stood exposed and naked and now you could see things about them as that there had been only three patterns the builder used and seeing the same house repeated cheapened it. And the houses shamefully acknowledged their new condition by becoming whatever sign was nailed to their fronts. Realtor. Sunshine Insurance, Inc. Massage. Artistic Framers.

And the gods never came. The streets never justified their widening. And the cars got smaller, shrank as the years passed. They had lost their chance. The cars were finally not what they had tried to be in the Greater American Imagination.

Remember how we deplored it. Think how long we hated the growing cars and it kept continuing to be just the same. Remember we were deploring it even as they were putting the sharp fins on the back that literally killed people by stabbing them, when all the driver meant was to back up.

That was when the cars were fighting back. And they lost. And in the wake of that war, a lot of litter and ugliness. And we got left with all those streets.

Her Name

It was 10:30 or 11:00 in the night, dinner finished long ago and since then the five or six of us had sat around the big square old time dinner table in the big square old time kitchen with coffee and beer and wine and smoking some dope. Another usual Northern California late at night stoned out brilliance, or so that's the feeling. The conversation like a dog that's good to go walking with, trit trot in one direction trit trot in another meandering circle, intent, nosing.

And in the midst of no reason for it that I can remember a bell rang very gently deep in my mind, a sweet sound for me rising from the valley floor. A reminder. I had missed something. I was short exactly one item on my list that had nothing else on it. I went mindless except for waiting to recognize it and my thinking went onto automatic scan and the only advantage I had was knowing it was in this room. My eyes moved as lightly as that bell had sounded, moved around the large room not quite lighting on anything while I waited to see if the memory that had announced itself would make a show.

In that kind of float of letting it happen I got up from the lighted island of the table and my feet carried me to a darker corner, to a stack of discarded newspapers that waited in their place between the fireplace and the kindling. I took up the top paper. I didn't have to read it. I looked consistently at the upper left corner on the right hand pages. I picked up the second paper. I found what I wanted on page three. And I still didn't know what it was I was after.

The article was three or four paragraphs about how police were looking for a doctor who had murdered his mother, his wife and his two adolescent children in one berserker rage. Blood everywhere. There were pictures of the two halfgrown victims smiling off the page the way victims often do, and the doctor was smiling too, alongside them. All of them looked pleased. The doctor was wearing a cap with a bill as if he were playing golf or set to go on a boat.

When I had read it through the first time I had wondered how they knew the doctor was the murderer and not a victim taken elsewhere. But really, that's probably, in that kind of no-cover-up, just the thing that would be known.

I reread the piece, following whatever that questing bit of my mind was and I found what I hadn't paid enough attention to.

The given name of the doctor's mother was Lobelia Amaryllis.

She must have been the only one ever with that name. Her mother loved flowers and passed on the sound of them to this infant she held in careful arms dressed in white lace to be named forever, the dress hanging down long, a cross made in holy water on the infant's forehead. A click of the camera and that placid infant gaze is held, printed in fading sepia, thrown forward in time to be dead on the floor in a pile of newspapers dated 1978; her name enroute to oblivion invoked this one last time by its own insistence.

The Child

After the child had been taken from the water. After someone had said it that the pool cover should be taken completely off to see whether he might have slipped through he was so small and the cover was removed and there he was in that strange element. There was a question of shock and something like discretion that could not let them use one of the long poles with nets on the end to reach into the water and manipulate the small body toward waiting hands at the poolside. That expedience was so possible. The poles were right there but. The owner jumped into the pool fully clothed and gathered the dead child to himself as if he hoped to save it back into life. As if it still might be that he would be in time. And the awkward moment was past. It had been dealt with humanly with an implication of hope and salvaging against the grief that was now all that could happen seeing the child's blue tinted face.

And the knowledge they all possessed had no hope left now. They all knew. Still they called the fire department and the ambulance that couldn't possibly arrive in less time than an hour and they laid the child in different positions and expelled the water from its lungs with pressure and breathed breath from their mouths into it and pressed that breath out again and breathed more useless air into it and pressed it out for a long time it seemed forever before the fire truck arrived with a resuscitator. And still no one said it, that he was dead. And when the small body was tidily on the bed in the ambulance and whisked away with tubes taped on the arms and injections still continuing and the ambulance attendant not looking at the mother, it would be so complicit what they knew together and no one would say now, not yet.

After all that and the inevitable outcome, the statement, and the clatter of true life drama when shocked eyes cannot understand the world that looks just the same.

After all that the young woman was alone again as if the child had never happened, as if death had annulled the child instead of ending it. And with the final drama faded and she felt the emptying there was also a fading to the earlier drama that had been happening before all this.

That earlier drama had begun with herself enamoured with the child's father, a young man of eighteen. She was also young, in her middle twenties, older than her lover therefore, significantly. It was her decisions that mattered.

She adored him, his eyes that were a light blue of clear skies, chestnut hair that sprang wiry around his face. She loved his laugh. He was beautiful and caught at her heartstrings so that it could never occur to her that he was not her own true gift. And she was tired of being alone.

She said when she became pregnant that she wanted the child as her own choice and that it was her responsibility. Her lover told her that he didn't want the child, that he was too young to be a father. He said that he wouldn't marry her and he asked her to have an abortion. She said the child was hers, it was her choice and she chose it. In her heart of hearts she thought the child would turn him. She carried the child and bore it, meaning to have its father.

It was true that she caught him in the wake of her decision. He trailed after her looking more and more sheepish. He daily looked less the man and more the boy. He was ashamed to be seen with her, with her great belly that laid such a claim to him as if his most private name were written there. He followed her shopping to carry the bags now that her belly was so big and he dawdled behind or walked swiftly ahead to the pick-up he had paid for with his own money made at his first real job doing construction work. He had been so proud of that truck. It had felt like a statement. A proof. And now it meant nothing. He cringed and ducked when his friends were in the store or on the street like an adolescent boy ashamed to be caught shopping with his mother.

For her part she suffered also. She had the bulk of her body and she could see that she might have made a mistake. She could see the ramifications resulting from her choice. But she would not acknowledge it. She told herself it was her lack of a figure that embarrassed him. It would all finally be the way she wanted it. When she was attractive again and they could go dancing, when the baby was here and a sweet thing to point up her femininity even more, when she would be outdoors in sunshine with the darling at her breast he would melt. It would be too much for him.

But she was simply wrong and found herself with the child she had insisted on and all the work of it. And the child was flawed, had a heart problem that must be operated on at a later date and until then there were things she must do about it. Her life was altered. Even with a figure she didn't get the response she had got earlier from men when she had been carefree. Men don't get turned on by women with kids, she thought.

She could get bitter about it. She felt more alone than ever, and let down. She felt jilted and resented it that her baby's father continued to live his old life almost untouched, while her life had changed so drastically. She would remind him that little boys need to know their father and he would be seen with the baby on his back in its little backpack that it travelled between the mother and father wearing, like a snail made of canvas cloth. She began to worry about the baby's heart, poor baby. Oh, the poor baby. And her face tightened up with it. She began to feel that her life was ruined, that the baby was an invalid, that she didn't have enough money. She began to ask the baby's father for money. Then she began to ask his father and his mother and even his grandmother for money. The money was never for herself. The money was for the baby. The baby needed money.

At first the father and his father and mother and grandmother gave her money when she asked but they realized over a period of time that the money went for dresses and babysitters so she could go dance at the bar. She longed for her earlier life.

The child got to be three years old before it was missed, then found, then treated ritually and finally allowed to be dead as if the statement was what killed it.

And now the drama was of herself bereaved. She was a mother who had lost her baby. It was true she felt it. She wished she had been a better mother, more loving to the poor baby.

She went to the bar now but seldom danced. She would sit in intense conversation usually with a man, with tears on her face. She would rehearse some aspect of the child's short life. The man she was talking to would have his arm around her shoulders or be holding her hand and she would be telling him her story as if she pleaded and when she would begin to cry he would hold her until she felt better and if she was too unstrung he would offer to drive her home and they would leave the bar together with little murmurs of farewell to and from the people they passed leaving as if they were leaving a graveside.

For awhile it looked dangerous, as if she might let the story carry her over the edge. She had a history of getting stuck in her own machinations, her imaginings. But at some point she did make the turn and she began to be more normal.

And after a couple of years had passed she could talk about how that time was without the complication of playing her role.

She was talking about her parents who had come to be with her for the memorial service. She had wanted to please them. She had borrowed a car for the time of their visit to drive them around in and she stocked the food they liked. She wanted it to be alright for a change. She thought for a visit like this one they would surely want to make it work.

'I took them up to Fort Bragg. I drove them all over. And for the whole drive my father never looked out of the window. All he did was look at a map of California he had on his lap. Oh, he did look up once. My mother said "Look Harry, there's a Mercedes," and he looked at the Mercedes. And that was it,' laughing.

She thought about it, how parents are, and looking very pretty she said, 'Can you believe it?' and laughed.

A Moral Tale

I was more than overdue to leave that job by the time it and me parted company. I wouldn't have been there in the first place but for desperation. Me and my two kids had been scraping by on forty dollars a week and that's the bottom of the barrel. You know how kids go through shoes and there's no way around it that they've got to have new ones.

I paid in close to sixty hours a week to get that forty dollars so when they offered me three hundred a month guaranteed against a percentage at the town's lousiest television station to be an Account Executive which is a piece of semantics that tries to make you sound like something more than a salesman I took it.

I think they thought I was 'hungry' enough to be a natural but I didn't live up to it. Get a hungry enough salesman and he'll get out there among his prospects and dig the money out with his teeth. Something like that. I just don't have the teeth for it.

Anyway I had enough accounts already on the air to justify my three hundred and I kept their copy and film and slides straight and told them when there was something they might be interested in but I wasn't a go-getter.

They got a new sales manager and it didn't take him more than a few days to see that my particular 'hungry' lacked the verve so he called me in one afternoon to give me my last chance.

He said he understood I was some kind of 'artistic' person and he translated that into 'Bohemian' without a look back. The next in line was 'free-love' in the sense of not caring much who you went to bed with and he stressed it that he didn't exactly mean 'free.'

He said I was a good looking woman and there were plenty of high ranking accounts that would throw to our side if their account executive was a willing good looking woman. And also, how did I feel about making extra bucks when out of town bigwigs hit the place and needed to see some night life. He was sure it was okay to discuss this with me having as I had a larger Bohemian sense of things. And needing the money as he knew I did. It looked like an arrangement that could work out all around.

It's always been a flaw in my moral makeup that I just don't get indignant and righteous and brain people and feel insulted when they come up with something interesting. It really interested me to hear this businessman laying out his kind of goods. Maybe I really do have a larger Bohemian sense of things. Anyway, when he finished his sales pitch I explained to him that being poor meant there were lots of things I couldn't afford. But I could keep on affording the luxury of only going to bed with somebody when I cared for them a lot and probably not even then.

'That doesn't cost me a dime,' I said.

We didn't bother mentioning that it had just cost me a lousy job and without further ado we were quits. We didn't bother shaking hands on it.

I went home and came back late that night, ten or so, to clean out my desk when I could be pretty sure nobody else would be there.

The television station sat at one end of a parking lot half a block big. The other end of the lot was held down by a giant orange like Peter Peter's pumpkin only this orange was big enough to hold half a dozen wives with their kids all seated in groups around little white plastic tables drinking Orange Julius and eating whatever their hearts desired. But not at ten o'clock in the night.

I went from the deserted office to the deserted orange.

Inside, the place was set up so that you always sat in bright lights in a window like a showcase ad for a customer in the process of being satisfied. I celebrated my newly departed job over a chili dog and a Pepsi with the bright overlighting bouncing back up into my face from the white plastic table.

The door swung open to let in one of my ex-colleagues. It was a hot night and his plump face was flushed red above his red necktie, white shirt and blue plaid sports coat. *He* would never be asked to enhance the station's hopes with a little night work. In fact gossip had it that he no longer had access to his own bed when his wife was in it. She was an athletic red head who spent her days playing golf and tennis and her nights whooping it up at the neighbourhood cocktail lounge with anybody but her red-faced husband.

He brought his cheeseburger and coffee and joined me. There was a certain amount of embarrassment in it, almost a kindness, as if he wanted me to know I was still okay in his books despite my being a loser.

He had that kind of face that works its way back to babyhood as jowls and chin and cheeks fill in and the hair falls out.

'I was thinner,' he said with a gesture toward himself, telling me this story, as though I might now see through him into that earlier person he spoke of. And it was true. I did see it. I saw him younger, thinner, more fresh, with the same slight bewilderment on his face that then, in a younger man, did not necessarily foretell as it did now that he would go to his grave bewildered and wondering.

We had never had any particular inclination to talk so it must have been my imminent departure that created that old atmosphere of ships passing in the night. However it came about it did and he told me this piece of himself, something sentimental to haul forward into a late night unlikely conversation.

After the war he had been stationed in Paris. He was a young officer and probably good looking. His face still held traces of that possibility.

The Opera had resumed and officers of the Allied Armies were given free passes. He and his friends went often. It was clear he had loved the spectacle. It was a place where the grand old world fought to regain itself. The women bared their shoulders and wore jewels if they had been able to keep them.

It is such a cliché this story. Throughout time in all the wars young men have been made seemly and acceptable by their uniforms. This story would never have happened to a man dressed in the jacket he now wore. It would never have occurred to him, it didn't occur even now to him, that he had been a valid fraud, costumed and glossed over, a sincere trap who meant it for the young woman he met. Naturally he described her as being from a 'really good family.'

My eyes must have shown the scepticism I felt. He described the young woman's mother, father, the style of life they maintained and gave him entry to. He was right. She had been from a good family.

When she knew that she was pregnant she told him and told him that she must tell her family.

Her young officer assumed that they would solve it by marrying.

'I'd have had to look a long way to come up with something better,' he said.

She tried to make him understand that she would never be allowed to marry a man capable of seducing her. Her father made it quite clear to him.

'People like that have a different kind of standards,' he wanted me to understand. It was another instance of their superior condition in his eyes.

'It's a different kind of morality,' he said. He was awed by it. Being snubbed by it proved its reality to him.

'I asked her to just run away with me, just go off and get married. She wouldn't do it.'

For as much longer as he was in Paris he spent long hours on a park bench near the house, hoping to see her. He did it in all kinds of weather. Finally he was transferred.

He had seen her only once after her parents laid their injunction down. She had come out of the house and he had seen her from a couple of blocks away. He had rushed to follow her. She went into a department store. He ran along the aisles and almost crashed against her.

They faced each other frozen in place.

He said her name, yearning towards her. He said, 'Her face was very tender.' He said, 'She looked so young.'

'No,' she said softly.

While he begged her she looked into him, miles of it between them, and said, 'No,' again. Then, without buying whatever she had come for, she turned and left him there and was gone.

But not quite.

Years later, years gone by, water over every dam, and it's night in the Orange Julius and here she was, invoked into being among the plastic tables, and here he was, aging, innocent and vulgar, his face forever bewildered.

He never knew what hit him.